Glencoe
Geometry

Integration
Applications
Connections

Study Guide Masters

GLENCOE
McGraw-Hill

New York, New York   Columbus, Ohio   Woodland Hills, California   Peoria, Illinois

Glencoe/McGraw-Hill

A Division of The McGraw-Hill Companies

Send all inquiries to:
Glencoe/McGraw-Hill
936 Eastwind Drive
Westerville, OH 43081-3374

Geometry
Study Guide Masters

ISBN: 0-02-825287-X

2 3 4 5 6 7 8 9 10   066   04 03 02 01 00 99 98 97

Contents

1–1

Study Guide

Integration: Algebra
The Coordinate Plane

Every point in the coordinate plane can be denoted by an ordered pair consisting of two numbers. The first number is the **x-coordinate**, and the second number is the **y-coordinate**.

> To determine the coordinates for a point, follow these steps.
> 1. Start at the origin and count the number of units to the right or left of the origin. The *positive direction* is to the right, and the *negative direction* is to the left.
> 2. Then count the number of units up or down. The positive direction is up, and the negative direction is down.
>   *Note:* If you do not move either right or left, the x-coordinate is 0. If you do not move up or down, the y-coordinate is 0.

Example: Write the ordered pair for each point shown at the right.

The ordered pair for R is $(2, 4)$.
The ordered pair for S is $(-3, 3)$.
The ordered pair for T is $(-4, -2)$.
The ordered pair for U is $(1, -4)$.
The ordered pair for W is $(0, 2)$.
The ordered pair for X is $(-2, 0)$.

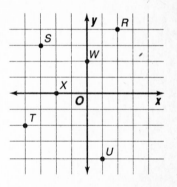

Write the ordered pair for each point shown at the right.

1. A
2. B
3. C

4. D
5. E
6. F

7. G
8. H
9. I

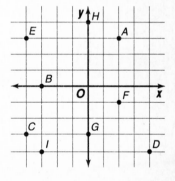

Graph each point on the coordinate plane.

10. $M(6, 4)$
11. $N(-5, 4)$

12. $P(-3, 5)$
13. $Q(6, 0)$

14. $J(0, -4)$
15. $K(7, -5)$

16. $Y(9, -3)$
17. $Z(-8, -5)$

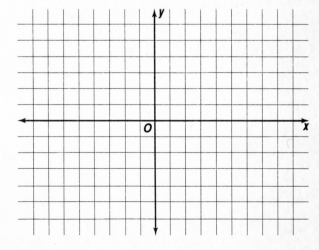

Study Guide

Integration: Algebra
The Coordinate Plane

Every point in the coordinate plane can be denoted by an ordered pair consisting of two numbers. The first number is the **x-coordinate**, and the second number is the **y-coordinate**.

To determine the coordinates for a point, follow these steps.
1. Start at the origin and count the number of units to the right or left of the origin. The *positive direction* is to the right, and the *negative direction* is to the left.
2. Then count the number of units up or down. The positive direction is up, and the negative direction is down.
   Note: If you do not move either right or left, the *x*-coordinate is 0. If you do not move up or down, the *y*-coordinate is 0.

Example: Write the ordered pair for each point shown at the right.

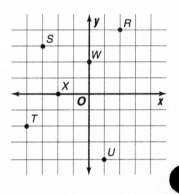

The ordered pair for R is $(2, 4)$.
The ordered pair for S is $(-3, 3)$.
The ordered pair for T is $(-4, -2)$.
The ordered pair for U is $(1, -4)$.
The ordered pair for W is $(0, 2)$.
The ordered pair for X is $(-2, 0)$.

Write the ordered pair for each point shown at the right.

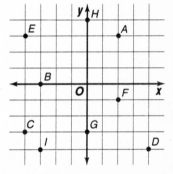

1. A $(2, 3)$ 2. B $(-3, 0)$ 3. C $(-4, -3)$

4. D $(4, -4)$ 5. E $(-4, 3)$ 6. F $(2, -1)$

7. G $(0, -3)$ 8. H $(0, 4)$ 9. I $(-3, -4)$

Graph each point on the coordinate plane.

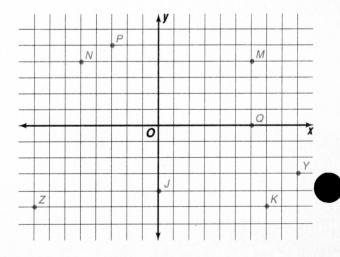

10. $M(6, 4)$ 11. $N(-5, 4)$

12. $P(-3, 5)$ 13. $Q(6, 0)$

14. $J(0, -4)$ 15. $K(7, -5)$

16. $Y(9, -3)$ 17. $Z(-8, -5)$

Geometry

Study Guide

Points, Lines, and Planes

Points, lines, and planes can be related in many different ways.
Figures can be used to show these relationships. When two
figures have one or more points in common, the figures are said
to **intersect**. When points lie on the same line, the points are
said to be **collinear**. When points lie in the same plane, the
points are said to be **coplanar**.

Example: Draw and label a figure for each relationship.

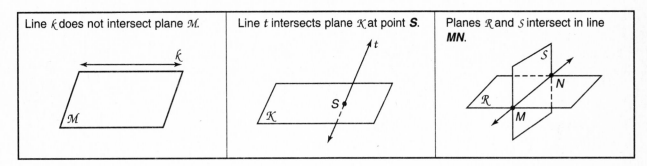

| Line k does not intersect plane $\mathcal{M}$. | Line t intersects plane $\mathcal{K}$ at point **S**. | Planes $\mathcal{R}$ and $\mathcal{S}$ intersect in line **MN**. |

Draw and label a figure for each relationship.

1. Lines JK and EF are not in plane $\mathcal{M}$, but intersect plane $\mathcal{M}$ at X.

2. Lines m and n intersect at point Q.

3. Points R, S, and T are in plane $\mathcal{M}$, but point W does not lie in plane $\mathcal{M}$.

4. The intersection of planes $\mathcal{A}$, $\mathcal{B}$, and $\mathcal{C}$ is line EF.

Refer to the figure at the right to answer each question.

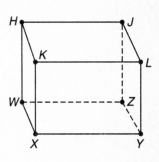

5. Are points H, J, K, and L coplanar?

6. Name three lines that intersect at X.

7. What points do plane $WXYZ$ and HW have in common?

8. Are points W, X, and Y collinear?

9. List the possibilities for naming a line contained in plane $WXKH$.

Study Guide

Points, Lines, and Planes

Points, lines, and planes can be related in many different ways.
Figures can be used to show these relationships. When two
figures have one or more points in common, the figures are said
to **intersect**. When points lie on the same line, the points are
said to be **collinear**. When points lie in the same plane, the
points are said to be **coplanar**.

Example: Draw and label a figure for each relationship.

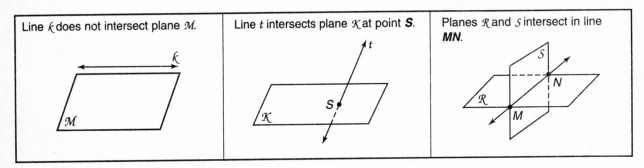

Draw and label a figure for each relationship.

1. Lines *JK* and *EF* are not in plane *M*,
but intersect plane *M* at *X*.

2. Lines *m* and *n* intersect at point *Q*.

3. Points *R*, *S*, and *T* are in plane *M*,
but point *W* does not lie in plane *M*.

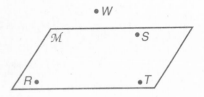

4. The intersection of planes *A*, *B*,
and *C* is line *EF*.

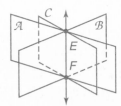

Refer to the figure at the right to answer each question.

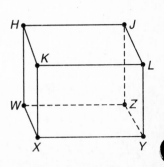

5. Are points *H*, *J*, *K*, and *L* coplanar? **yes**

6. Name three lines that intersect at *X*. $\overleftrightarrow{WX}$, $\overleftrightarrow{KX}$, $\overleftrightarrow{XY}$

7. What points do plane *WXYZ* and *HW* have in common? **W**

8. Are points *W*, *X*, and *Y* collinear? **no**

9. List the possibilities for naming a line contained in plane
WXKH. $\overleftrightarrow{HK}$, $\overleftrightarrow{KH}$, $\overleftrightarrow{HW}$, $\overleftrightarrow{WH}$, $\overleftrightarrow{WX}$, $\overleftrightarrow{XW}$, $\overleftrightarrow{XK}$, $\overleftrightarrow{KX}$, $\overleftrightarrow{KW}$, $\overleftrightarrow{WK}$, $\overleftrightarrow{HX}$, $\overleftrightarrow{XH}$

NAME _____ DATE _____

Study Guide

Integration: Algebra
Using Formulas

The following four-step plan can be used to solve any problem.

Problem-Solving Plan	
1. *Explore* the problem.	Identify what you want to know.
2. *Plan* the solution.	Choose a strategy.
3. *Solve* the problem.	Use the strategy to solve the problem.
4. *Examine* the solution.	Check your answer.

When finding a solution, it may be necessary to use a formula. Two useful formulas are the area formula and perimeter formula for a rectangle.

Area of a Rectangle	The formula for the area of a rectangle is $A = \ell w$, where A represents the area expressed in square units, ℓ represents the length, and w represents the width.
Perimeter of a Rectangle	The formula for the perimeter of a rectangle is $P = 2\ell + 2w$, where P represents the perimeter, ℓ represents the length and w represents the width.

Examples

1 Find the perimeter and area of the rectangle at the right.

$P = 2\ell + 2w$
$\quad = 2(7) + 2(2)$
$\quad = 14 + 4 \text{ or } 18$
The perimeter is 18 inches.

$A = \ell w$
$\quad = 7 \cdot 2 \text{ or } 14$
The area is 14 in^2.

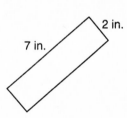

2 Find the width of a rectangle whose area is 52 cm^2 and whose length is 13 cm.

$A = \ell w$
$\dfrac{52}{13} = \dfrac{13w}{13}$
$4 = w$
The width is 4 cm.

Find the perimeter and area of each rectangle.

1.

6 cm

4 cm

2.

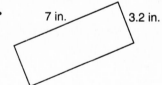

7 in.   3.2 in.

3.

8 yd

8 yd

Find the missing measure in each formula.

4. $\ell = 3$, $w = 7$, $P = \underline{\ ?\ }$

5. $w = 5.2$, $\ell = 6.5$, $A = \underline{\ ?\ }$

6. $w = 4$, $A = 36$, $\ell = \underline{\ ?\ }$

7. $P = 65$, $\ell = 18$, $w = \underline{\ ?\ }$

Geometry

Study Guide

Integration: Algebra
Using Formulas

The following four-step plan can be used to solve any problem.

Problem-Solving Plan	
1. *Explore* the problem.	Identify what you want to know.
2. *Plan* the solution.	Choose a strategy.
3. *Solve* the problem.	Use the strategy to solve the problem.
4. *Examine* the solution.	Check your answer.

When finding a solution, it may be necessary to use a formula. Two useful formulas are the area formula and perimeter formula for a rectangle.

Area of a Rectangle	The formula for the area of a rectangle is $A = \ell w$, where A represents the area expressed in square units, ℓ represents the length, and w represents the width.
Perimeter of a Rectangle	The formula for the perimeter of a rectangle is $P = 2\ell + 2w$, where P represents the perimeter, ℓ represents the length and w represents the width.

Examples

1 Find the perimeter and area of the rectangle at the right.

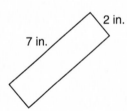

$P = 2\ell + 2w$
$\quad = 2(7) + 2(2)$
$\quad = 14 + 4 \text{ or } 18$
The perimeter is 18 inches.

$A = \ell w$
$\quad = 7 \cdot 2 \text{ or } 14$
The area is 14 in^2.

2 Find the width of a rectangle whose area is 52 cm^2 and whose length is 13 cm.

$A = \ell w$
$\dfrac{52}{13} = \dfrac{13w}{13}$
$4 = w$
The width is 4 cm.

Find the perimeter and area of each rectangle.

1.

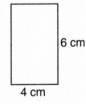

4 cm, 6 cm

20 cm, 24 cm²

2.

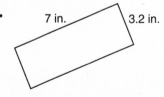

7 in., 3.2 in.

20.4 in., 22.4 in²

3.

8 yd, 8 yd

32 yd, 64 yd²

Find the missing measure in each formula.

4. $\ell = 3$, $w = 7$, $P = \underline{\ ?\ }$ **20**
6. $w = 4$, $A = 36$, $\ell = \underline{\ ?\ }$ **9**

5. $w = 5.2$, $\ell = 6.5$, $A = \underline{\ ?\ }$ **33.8**
7. $P = 65$, $\ell = 18$, $w = \underline{\ ?\ }$ **14.5**

Study Guide

Measuring Segments

To find the distance between two points, there are two situations to consider.

Distance on a Number Line	Distance in the Coordinate Plane	
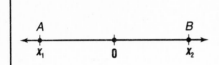 $$AB = |x_2 - x_1|$$ **Example:** Find AB on the number line shown below. 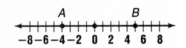 $$AB = |5 - (-4)|$$ $$= |9|$$ $$= 9$$	**Pythagorean Theorem:** $$(AB)^2 = (AC)^2 + (BC)^2$$ **Example:** Find the distance from $A(-3, -1)$ to $B(1, 2)$ using the Pythagorean Theorem. 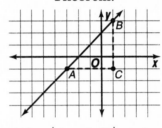 $$AC = |1 - (-3)| \text{ or } 4$$ $$BC = |2 - (-1)| \text{ or } 3$$ $$(AB)^2 = 4^2 + 3^2$$ $$= 16 + 9 \text{ or } 25$$ $$AB = \sqrt{25}$$ $$= 5$$	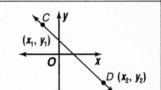 **Distance Formula:** $$CD = \sqrt{(x_2 - x_1)^2 + (y_2 - y_1)^2}$$ **Example:** Find the distance from $C(-3, 2)$ to $D(4, -1)$ using the distance formula. 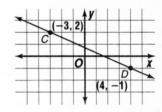 $$CD = \sqrt{(-3 - 4)^2 + [2 - (-1)]^2}$$ $$= \sqrt{(-7)^2 + 3^2}$$ $$= \sqrt{49 + 9}$$ $$= \sqrt{58}$$ $$\approx 7.62$$

Refer to the number line below to find each measure.

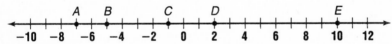

1. AC 2. BC 3. CD 4. AE

5. AB 6. DE 7. BE 8. CE

Refer to the coordinate plane at the right to find each measure. Round your measures to the nearest hundredth.

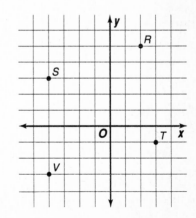

9. RS 10. RT

11. RV 12. VS

13. VT 14. ST

Geometry

NAME_____ DATE _____

Study Guide

Measuring Segments

To find the distance between two points, there are two situations to consider.

Distance on a Number Line	Distance in the Coordinate Plane	
 $$AB = \lvert x_2 - x_1 \rvert$$ **Example:** Find AB on the number line shown below. $AB = \lvert 5 - (-4) \rvert$ $= \lvert 9 \rvert$ $= 9$	**Pythagorean Theorem:** $$(AB)^2 = (AC)^2 + (BC)^2$$ **Example:** Find the distance from $A(-3, -1)$ to $B(1, 2)$ using the Pythagorean Theorem. 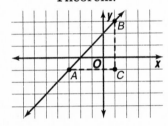 $AC = \lvert 1 - (-3) \rvert$ or 4 $BC = \lvert 2 - (-1) \rvert$ or 3 $(AB)^2 = 4^2 + 3^2$ $= 16 + 9$ or 25 $AB = \sqrt{25}$ $= 5$	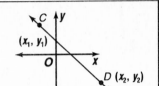 **Distance Formula:** $$CD = \sqrt{(x_2 - x_1)^2 + (y_2 - y_1)^2}$$ **Example:** Find the distance from $C(-3, 2)$ to $D(4, -1)$ using the distance formula. 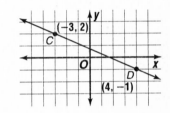 $CD = \sqrt{(-3 - 4)^2 + [2 - (-1)]^2}$ $= \sqrt{(-7)^2 + 3^2}$ $= \sqrt{49 + 9}$ $= \sqrt{58}$ ≈ 7.62

Refer to the number line below to find each measure.

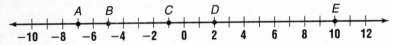

1. AC 6   2. BC 4   3. CD 3   4. AE 17

5. AB 2   6. DE 8   7. BE 15   8. CE 11

Refer to the coordinate plane at the right to find each measure. Round your measures to the nearest hundredth.

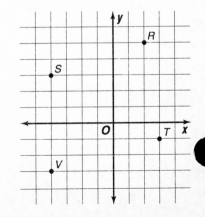

9. RS 6.32   10. RT 6.08

11. RV 10.00   12. VS 6.00

13. VT 7.28   14. ST 8.06

Geometry

NAME_____ DATE _____

Study Guide

Midpoints and Segment Congruence

There are two situations in which you may need to find the midpoint of a segment.

Midpoint on a Number Line	Midpoint in the Coordinate Plane
The coordinate of the midpoint of a segment whose endpoints have coordinates a and b is $\frac{a+b}{2}$. **Example:**  The coordinate of the midpoint of $\overline{RS}$ is $\frac{-3+9}{2}$ or 3.	The coordinates of the midpoint of a segment whose endpoints have coordinates (x_1, y_1) and (x_2, y_2) are $\left(\frac{x_1+x_2}{2}, \frac{y_1+y_2}{2}\right)$. **Example:** 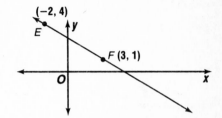 The coordinates of the midpoint of EF are $\left(\frac{-2+3}{2}, \frac{4+1}{2}\right)$ or $\left(\frac{1}{2}, \frac{5}{2}\right)$.

Use the number line below to find the coordinates of the midpoint of each segment.

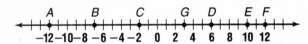

1. $\overline{AB}$

2. $\overline{BC}$

3. $\overline{CE}$

4. $\overline{DE}$

5. $\overline{AE}$

6. $\overline{FC}$

7. $\overline{GE}$

8. $\overline{BF}$

Refer to the coordinate plane at the right to find the coordinates of the midpoint of each segment.

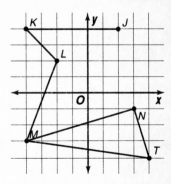

9. $\overline{JK}$

10. $\overline{KL}$

11. $\overline{LM}$

12. $\overline{MN}$

13. $\overline{NT}$

14. $\overline{MT}$

Geometry

Study Guide

Midpoints and Segment Congruence

There are two situations in which you may need to find the midpoint of a segment.

Midpoint on a Number Line	Midpoint in the Coordinate Plane
The coordinate of the midpoint of a segment whose endpoints have coordinates a and b is $\frac{a+b}{2}$.	The coordinates of the midpoint of a segment whose endpoints have coordinates (x_1, y_1) and (x_2, y_2) are $\left(\frac{x_1 + x_2}{2}, \frac{y_1 + y_2}{2}\right)$.
Example:  The coordinate of the midpoint of $\overline{RS}$ is $\frac{-3+9}{2}$ or 3.	*Example:* 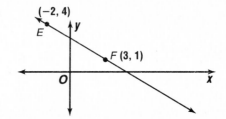 The coordinates of the midpoint of EF are $\left(\frac{-2+3}{2}, \frac{4+1}{2}\right)$ or $\left(\frac{1}{2}, \frac{5}{2}\right)$.

Use the number line below to find the coordinates of the midpoint of each segment.

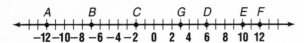

1. $\overline{AB}$ $-\frac{19}{2}$

2. $\overline{BC}$ $-\frac{9}{2}$

3. $\overline{CE}$ 4

4. $\overline{DE}$ 8

5. $\overline{AE}$ −1

6. $\overline{FC}$ 5

7. $\overline{GE}$ $\frac{13}{2}$

8. $\overline{BF}$ $\frac{5}{2}$

Refer to the coordinate plane at the right to find the coordinates of the midpoint of each segment.

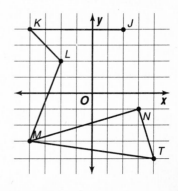

9. $\overline{JK}$ (−1, 4)

10. $\overline{KL}$ (−3, 3)

11. $\overline{LM}$ $\left(-3, -\frac{1}{2}\right)$

12. $\overline{MN}$ $\left(-\frac{1}{2}, -2\right)$

13. $\overline{NT}$ $\left(\frac{7}{2}, -\frac{5}{2}\right)$

14. $\overline{MT}$ $\left(0, -\frac{7}{2}\right)$

Study Guide

Exploring Angles

An angle is formed by two noncollinear rays with a common endpoint. You could name the angle in the figure at the right as $\angle S$, $\angle RST$, $\angle TSR$, or $\angle 1$.

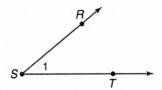

When two or more angles have a common vertex, you need to use either three letters or a number to name the angles. Make sure there is no doubt which angle your name describes.

A **right angle** is an angle whose measure is 90. Angles smaller than a right angle are **acute angles**. Angles larger than a right angle are **obtuse angles**. A **straight angle** has a measure of 180.

According to the Angle Addition Postulate, if D is in the interior of $\angle ABC$, then $m\angle ABD + m\angle DBC = m\angle ABC$.

Example: In the figure at the right, $m\angle ABC = 160$, $m\angle 1 = x + 14$, and $m\angle 2 = 3x - 10$. Find the value of x.

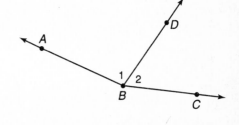

$$m\angle 1 + m\angle 2 = m\angle ABC$$
$$(x + 14) + (3x - 10) = m\angle ABC$$
$$4x + 4 = 160$$
$$4x = 156$$
$$x = 39$$

For Exercises 1–5, refer to the figure at the right.

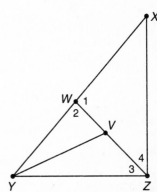

1. Do $\angle 3$ and $\angle Z$ name the same angle? Explain.

2. List all the angles that have W as the vertex.

3. Name a straight angle.

4. If $m\angle WYV = 4x - 2$, $m\angle VYZ = 2x - 5$, and $m\angle WYZ = 77$, find the measurements of $\angle WYV$ and $\angle VYZ$.

5. Does $\angle YVW$ appear to be acute, obtuse, right, or straight?

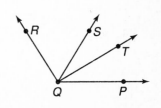

6. In the figure at the right, if $\overrightarrow{QS}$ bisects $\angle RQP$, $m\angle RQS = 2x + 10$, and $m\angle SQP = 3x - 18$, find $m\angle SQR$.

Study Guide

Exploring Angles

An angle is formed by two noncollinear rays with a common endpoint. You could name the angle in the figure at the right as ∠ *S*, ∠ *RST*, ∠ *TSR*, or ∠1.

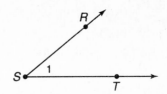

When two or more angles have a common vertex, you need to use either three letters or a number to name the angles. Make sure there is no doubt which angle your name describes.

A **right angle** is an angle whose measure is 90. Angles smaller than a right angle are **acute angles**. Angles larger than a right angle are **obtuse angles**. A **straight angle** has a measure of 180.

According to the Angle Addition Postulate, if *D* is in the interior of ∠*ABC*, then $m\angle ABD + m\angle DBC = m\angle ABC$.

Example: In the figure at the right,
$m\angle ABC = 160$, $m\angle 1 = x + 14$, and
$m\angle 2 = 3x - 10$. Find the value of *x*.

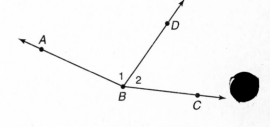

$$m\angle 1 + m\angle 2 = m\angle ABC$$
$$(x + 14) + (3x - 10) = m\angle ABC$$
$$4x + 4 = 160$$
$$4x = 156$$
$$x = 39$$

For Exercises 1–5, refer to the figure at the right.

1. Do ∠3 and ∠*Z* name the same angle? Explain. **Not necessarily; *Z* is the vertex of three angles, ∠3, ∠4, and ∠*YZX*.**

2. List all the angles that have *W* as the vertex. **∠*YWX*, ∠*YWZ*, or ∠2, ∠*XWZ* or ∠1**

3. Name a straight angle. **∠*YWX* or ∠*WVZ***

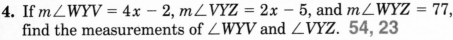

4. If $m\angle WYV = 4x - 2$, $m\angle VYZ = 2x - 5$, and $m\angle WYZ = 77$, find the measurements of ∠*WYV* and ∠*VYZ*. **54, 23**

5. Does ∠*YVW* appear to be acute, obtuse, right, or straight? **acute**

6. In the figure at the right, if $\overrightarrow{QS}$ bisects ∠*RQP*, $m\angle RQS = 2x + 10$, and $m\angle SQP = 3x - 18$, find $m\angle SQR$. **66**

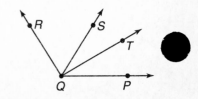

Angle Relationships

The following table identifies several different types of angles that occur in pairs.

Pairs of Angles		
Special Name	**Definition**	**Examples**
adjacent angles	angles in the same plane that have a common vertex and a common side, but no common interior points	$\angle EHF$ and $\angle FHG$ are adjacent angles.
vertical angles	two nonadjacent angles formed by two intersecting lines (Vertical angles are congruent.)	$\angle 1$ and $\angle 3$ are vertical angles. $\angle 2$ and $\angle 4$ are vertical angles. $\angle 1 \cong \angle 3, \angle 2 \cong \angle 4$
linear pair	adjacent angles whose noncommon sides are opposite rays	$\angle 5$ and $\angle 6$ form a linear pair.
complementary angles	two angles whose measures have a sum of 90	$30°$ $60°$
supplementary angles	two angles whose measures have a sum of 180	$20°$ $160°$

Identify each pair of angles as adjacent, vertical, complementary, supplementary, and/or as a linear pair.

1. $\angle 1$ and $\angle 2$

2. $\angle 1$ and $\angle 4$

3. $\angle 3$ and $\angle 4$

4. $\angle 1$ and $\angle 5$

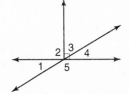

Find the value of x.

5.

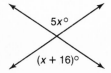

$5x°$

$(x + 16)°$

6.

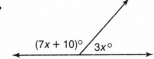

$(7x + 10)°$ $3x°$

7.

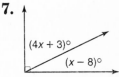

$(4x + 3)°$

$(x - 8)°$

1-7

Study Guide

Angle Relationships

The following table identifies several different types of angles
that occur in pairs.

Pairs of Angles		
Special Name	**Definition**	**Examples**
adjacent angles	angles in the same plane that have a common vertex and a common side, but no common interior points	$\angle EHF$ and $\angle FHG$ are adjacent angles.
vertical angles	two nonadjacent angles formed by two intersecting lines (Vertical angles are congruent.)	$\angle 1$ and $\angle 3$ are vertical angles. $\angle 2$ and $\angle 4$ are vertical angles. $\angle 1 \cong \angle 3$, $\angle 2 \cong \angle 4$
linear pair	adjacent angles whose noncommon sides are opposite rays	$\angle 5$ and $\angle 6$ form a linear pair.
complementary angles	two angles whose measures have a sum of 90	$30°$ $60°$
supplementary angles	two angles whose measures have a sum of 180	$20°$ $160°$

***Identify each pair of angles as adjacent, vertical,
complementary, supplementary, and/or as a linear pair.***

1. $\angle 1$ and $\angle 2$ adjacent

2. $\angle 1$ and $\angle 4$
vertical

3. $\angle 3$ and $\angle 4$ adjacent, complementary

4. $\angle 1$ and $\angle 5$
adjacent,
supplementary, linear pair

Find the value of x.

5.
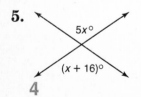
$5x°$
$(x + 16)°$
4

6.
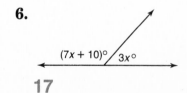
$(7x + 10)°$ $3x°$
17

7.
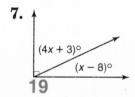
$(4x + 3)°$
$(x − 8)°$
19

© Glencoe/McGraw-Hill

T7

Geometry

Study Guide

Inductive Reasoning and Conjecturing

In daily life, you frequently look at several specific situations and reach a general conclusion based on these specific cases. For example, you might receive excellent service in a restaurant several times and conclude that the service is always good. Of course, you are not guaranteed that the service will be good when you return.

This type of reasoning, in which you look at several facts and then make an educated guess based on these facts, is called **inductive reasoning**. The educated guess is called a **conjecture**. Not all conjectures are true. When you find an example that shows the conjecture is false, this example is called a **counterexample**.

Example: Determine if the conjecture is *true* or *false* based on the given information. Explain your answer and give a counterexample if false.

Given: $\overline{AB} \cong \overline{BC}$
Conjecture: B is the midpoint of AC.

In the figure, $\overline{AB} \cong \overline{BC}$, but B is not the midpoint of $\overline{AC}$.
So the conjecture is false.

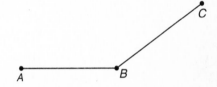

Determine if each conjecture is <u>true</u> or <u>false</u> based on the given information. Explain your answer and give a counterexample for any false conjecture.

1. **Given:** Collinear points D, E, and F.
   Conjecture: $DE + EF = DF$.

2. **Given:** $\angle A$ and $\angle B$ are supplementary.
   Conjecture: $\angle A$ and $\angle B$ are adjacent angles.

3. **Given:** $\angle D$ and $\angle F$ are supplementary.
             $\angle E$ and $\angle F$ are supplementary.
   Conjecture: $\angle D \cong \angle E$

4. **Given:** $\overline{AB}$ is perpendicular to $\overline{BC}$.
   Conjecture: $\angle ABC$ is a right angle.

NAME_____ DATE _____

Study Guide

Inductive Reasoning and Conjecturing

In daily life, you frequently look at several specific situations and reach a general conclusion based on these specific cases. For example, you might receive excellent service in a restaurant several times and conclude that the service is always good. Of course, you are not guaranteed that the service will be good when you return.

This type of reasoning, in which you look at several facts and then make an educated guess based on these facts, is called **inductive reasoning**. The educated guess is called a **conjecture**. Not all conjectures are true. When you find an example that shows the conjecture is false, this example is called a **counterexample**.

Example: Determine if the conjecture is *true* or *false* based on the given information. Explain your answer and give a counterexample if false.

Given: $\overline{AB} \cong \overline{BC}$
Conjecture: B is the midpoint of AC.

In the figure, $\overline{AB} \cong \overline{BC}$, but B is not the midpoint of $\overline{AC}$. So the conjecture is false.

Determine if each conjecture is <u>true</u> or <u>false</u> based on the given information. Explain your answer and give a counterexample for any false conjecture.

1. **Given:** Collinear points D, E, and F.
   Conjecture: $DE + EF = DF$. **False; if F is between D and E (or if D is between E and F), then DE + EF ≠ DF.**

2. **Given:** $\angle A$ and $\angle B$ are supplementary.
   Conjecture: $\angle A$ and $\angle B$ are adjacent angles. **False; if ∠A and ∠B do not have the same vertex, they cannot be adjacent.**

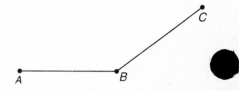

3. **Given:** $\angle D$ and $\angle F$ are supplementary.
   $\angle E$ and $\angle F$ are supplementary.
   Conjecture: $\angle D \cong \angle E$ **True; if m∠F = 25, them m∠D = 180 − 25 or 155 and m∠E = 180 − 25 or 155. Since m∠D = m∠E, then ∠D ≅ ∠E.**

4. **Given:** $\overline{AB}$ is perpendicular to $\overline{BC}$.
   Conjecture: $\angle ABC$ is a right angle. **True, if the sides of an angle are perpendicular, the angle is a right angle.**

Study Guide

If-Then Statements and Postulates

If-then statements are commonly used in everyday life. For example, an advertisement might say, "If you buy our product, then you will be happy." Notice that an if-then statement has two parts, a *hypothesis* (the part following "if") and a *conclusion* (the part following "then").

New statements can be formed from the original statement.

Statement	$p \rightarrow q$
Converse	$q \rightarrow p$
Inverse	$\sim p \rightarrow \sim q$
Contrapositive	$\sim q \rightarrow \sim p$

Example: Rewrite the following statement in if-then form. Then write the converse, inverse, and contrapositive.

All elephants are mammals.

If-then form:	If an animal is an elephant, then it is a mammal.
Converse:	If an animal is a mammal, then it is an elephant.
Inverse:	If an animal is not an elephant, then it is not a mammal.
Contrapositive:	If an animal is not a mammal, then it is not an elephant.

Identify the hypothesis and conclusion of each conditional statement.

1. If today is Monday, then tomorrow is Tuesday.

2. If a truck weighs 2 tons, then it weighs 4000 pounds.

Write each conditional statement in if-then form.

3. All chimpanzees love bananas.

4. Collinear points lie on the same line.

Write the converse, inverse, and contrapositive of each conditional.

5. If an animal is a fish, then it can swim.

6. All right angles are congruent.

NAME_____ DATE _____

Study Guide

If-Then Statements and Postulates

If-then statements are commonly used in everyday life. For example, an advertisement might say, "If you buy our product, then you will be happy." Notice that an if-then statement has two parts, a *hypothesis* (the part following "if") and a *conclusion* (the part following "then").

New statements can be formed from the original statement.

Statement	$p \rightarrow q$
Converse	$q \rightarrow p$
Inverse	$\sim p \rightarrow \sim q$
Contrapositive	$\sim q \rightarrow \sim p$

Example: Rewrite the following statement in if-then form. Then write the converse, inverse, and contrapositive.

All elephants are mammals.

If-then form:	If an animal is an elephant, then it is a mammal.
Converse:	If an animal is a mammal, then it is an elephant.
Inverse:	If an animal is not an elephant, then it is not a mammal.
Contrapositive:	If an animal is not a mammal, then it is not an elephant.

Identify the hypothesis and conclusion of each conditional statement.

1. If today is Monday, then tomorrow is Tuesday. H: today is Monday; C: tomorrow is Tuesday

2. If a truck weighs 2 tons, then it weighs 4000 pounds. H: a truck weighs 2 tons; C: it weighs 4000 pounds

Write each conditional statement in if-then form.

3. All chimpanzees love bananas. If an animal is a chimpanzee, then it loves bananas.

4. Collinear points lie on the same line. If points are collinear, then they lie on the same line.

Write the converse, inverse, and contrapositive of each conditional.

5. If an animal is a fish, then it can swim. Converse: If an animal can swim, then it is a fish. Inverse: If an animal is not a fish, then it cannot swim. Contrapositive: If an animal cannot swim, then it is not a fish.

6. All right angles are congruent. Converse: If angles are congruent, then they are right angles. Inverse: If angles are not right angles, then they are not congruent. Contrapositive: If angles are not congruent, then they are not right angles.

     Geometry

2-3

Study Guide

Deductive Reasoning

Two important laws used frequently in deductive reasoning are the **Law of Detachment** and the **Law of Syllogism**. In both cases you reach conclusions based on if-then statements.

Law of Detachment	Law of Syllogism
If $p \rightarrow q$ is a true conditional and p is true, then q is true.	If $p \rightarrow q$ and $q \rightarrow r$ are true conditionals, then $p \rightarrow r$ is also true.

Example: Determine if statement (3) follows from statements (1) and (2) by the Law of Detachment or the Law of Syllogism. If it does, state which law was used.

(1) If you break an item in a store, you must pay for it.
(2) Jill broke a vase in Potter's Gift Shop.
(3) Jill must pay for the vase.

Yes, statement (3) follows from statements (1) and (2) by the Law of Detachment.

Determine if a valid conclusion can be reached from the two true statements using the Law of Detachment or the Law of Syllogism. If a valid conclusion is possible, state it and the law that is used. If a valid conclusion does not follow, write no conclusion.

1. (1) If a number is a whole number, then it is an integer.
   (2) If a number is an integer, then it is a rational number.

2. (1) If a dog eats Dogfood Delights, the dog is happy.
   (2) Fido is a happy dog.

3. (1) If people live in Manhattan, then they live in New York.
   (2) If people live in New York, then they live in the United States.

4. (1) Angles that are complementary have measures with a sum of 90.
   (2) $\angle A$ and $\angle B$ are complementary.

5. (1) All fish can swim.
   (2) Fonzo can swim.

6. **Look for a Pattern** Find the next number in the list 83, 77, 71, 65, 59 and make a conjecture about the pattern.

Study Guide

Deductive Reasoning

Two important laws used frequently in deductive reasoning are the **Law of Detachment** and the **Law of Syllogism**. In both cases you reach conclusions based on if-then statements.

Law of Detachment	Law of Syllogism
If $p \rightarrow q$ is a true conditional and p is true, then q is true.	If $p \rightarrow q$ and $q \rightarrow r$ are true conditionals, then $p \rightarrow r$ is also true.

Example: Determine if statement (3) follows from statements (1) and (2) by the Law of Detachment or the Law of Syllogism. If it does, state which law was used.

(1) If you break an item in a store, you must pay for it.
(2) Jill broke a vase in Potter's Gift Shop.
(3) Jill must pay for the vase.

Yes, statement (3) follows from statements (1) and (2) by the Law of Detachment.

Determine if a valid conclusion can be reached from the two true statements using the Law of Detachment or the Law of Syllogism. If a valid conclusion is possible, state it and the law that is used. If a valid conclusion does not follow, write <u>no conclusion</u>.

1. (1) If a number is a whole number, then it is an integer.
   (2) If a number is an integer, then it is a rational number. **If a number is a whole number, then it is a rational number; syllogism.**

2. (1) If a dog eats Dogfood Delights, the dog is happy.
   (2) Fido is a happy dog. **no conclusion**

3. (1) If people live in Manhattan, then they live in New York.
   (2) If people live in New York, then they live in the United States. **If people live in Manhattan, then they live in the United States; syllogism.**

4. (1) Angles that are complementary have measures with a sum of 90.
   (2) $\angle A$ and $\angle B$ are complementary. **$m\angle A + m\angle B = 90$; detachment**

5. (1) All fish can swim.
   (2) Fonzo can swim. **no conclusion**

6. **Look for a Pattern** Find the next number in the list 83, 77, 71, 65, 59 and make a conjecture about the pattern. **53; each number is 6 less than the preceding one.**

2–4

Study Guide

Integration: Algebra
Using Proof in Algebra

Many rules from algebra are used in geometry.

Properties of Equality for Real Numbers	
Reflexive Property	$a = a$
Symmetric Property	If $a = b$, then $b = a$.
Transitive Property	If $a = b$ and $b = c$, then $a = c$.
Addition Property	If $a = b$, then $a + c = b + c$.
Subtraction Property	If $a = b$, then $a - c = b - c$.
Multiplication Property	If $a = b$, then $a \cdot c = b \cdot c$.
Division Property	If $a = b$ and $c \neq 0$, then $\frac{a}{c} = \frac{b}{c}$.
Substitution Property	If $a = b$, then a may be replaced by b in any equation or expression.
Distributive Property	$a(b + c) = ab + ac$

Example: Prove that if $4x - 8 = -8$, then $x = 0$.

Given: $4x - 8 = -8$

Prove: $x = 0$

Proof:

Statements	Reasons
a. $4x - 8 = -8$	**a.** Given
b. $4x = 0$	**b.** Addition Property (=)
c. $x = 0$	**c.** Division Property (=)

Name the property that justifies each statement.

1. Prove that if $\frac{3}{5}x = -9$, then $x = -15$.

Given: $\frac{3}{5}x = -9$

Prove: $x = -15$

Proof:

Statements	Reasons
a. $\frac{3}{5}x = -9$	**a.** _____
b. $3x = -45$	**b.** _____
c. $x = -15$	**c.** _____

2. Prove that if $3x - 2 = x - 8$, then $x = -3$.

Given: $3x - 2 = x - 8$

Prove: $x = -3$

Proof:

Statements	Reasons
a. $3x - 2 = x - 8$	**a.** _____
b. $2x - 2 = -8$	**b.** _____
c. $2x = -6$	**c.** _____
d. $x = -3$	**d.** _____

NAME_____ DATE _____

Study Guide

Integration: Algebra
Using Proof in Algebra

Many rules from algebra are used in geometry.

Properties of Equality for Real Numbers	
Reflexive Property	$a = a$
Symmetric Property	If $a = b$, then $b = a$.
Transitive Property	If $a = b$ and $b = c$, then $a = c$.
Addition Property	If $a = b$, then $a + c = b + c$.
Subtraction Property	If $a = b$, then $a - c = b - c$.
Multiplication Property	If $a = b$, then $a \cdot c = b \cdot c$.
Division Property	If $a = b$ and $c \neq 0$, then $\frac{a}{c} = \frac{b}{c}$.
Substitution Property	If $a = b$, then a may be replaced by b in any equation or expression.
Distributive Property	$a(b + c) = ab + ac$

Example: Prove that if $4x - 8 = {}^-8$, then $x = 0$.

Given: $4x - 8 = {}^-8$

Prove: $x = 0$

Proof:

Statements	Reasons
a. $4x - 8 = {}^-8$	**a.** Given
b. $4x = 0$	**b.** Addition Property $(=)$
c. $x = 0$	**c.** Division Property $(=)$

Name the property that justifies each statement.

1. Prove that if $\frac{3}{5}x = {}^-9$, then $x = {}^-15$.

Given: $\frac{3}{5}x = {}^-9$

Prove: $x = {}^-15$

Proof:

Statements	Reasons
a. $\frac{3}{5}x = {}^-9$	**a.** Given
b. $3x = {}^-45$	**b.** Multiplication Property $(=)$
c. $x = {}^-15$	**c.** Division Property $(=)$

2. Prove that if $3x - 2 = x - 8$, then $x = {}^-3$.

Given: $3x - 2 = x - 8$

Prove: $x = {}^-3$

Proof:

Statements	Reasons
a. $3x - 2 = x - 8$	**a.** Given
b. $2x - 2 = {}^-8$	**b.** Subtraction Property $(=)$
c. $2x = {}^-6$	**c.** Addition Property $(=)$
d. $x = {}^-3$	**d.** Division Property $(=)$

Study Guide

Verifying Segment Relationships

Proofs in geometry follow the same format that you used in Lesson 2–4. The steps in a two-column proof are arranged so that each step follows logically from the preceding one. The reasons can be given information, definitions, postulates of geometry, or rules of algebra. You may also use information that is safe to assume from a given figure.

Example: Write a two-column proof.

Given: $\overline{BC} \cong \overline{DE}$

Prove: $AC = AB + DE$

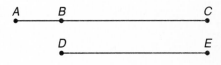

Proof:

Statements	Reasons
a. $\overline{BC} \cong \overline{DE}$	a. Given
b. $BC = DE$	b. Definition of congruent segments
c. $AC = AB + BC$	c. Segment Addition Postulate
d. $AC = AB + BC$	d. Substitution Property (=)

Complete each proof by naming the property that justifies each statement.

1. **Given:** M is the midpoint of $\overline{AB}$.
   B is the midpoint of $\overline{MD}$.

   Prove: $MD = 2MB$

   Proof:

Statements	Reasons
a. M is the midpoint of $\overline{AB}$. B is the midpoint of $\overline{MD}$.	a. _____
b. $AM = MB$ $MB = BD$	b. _____
c. $MD = MB + BD$	c. _____
d. $MD = MB + MB$	d. _____
e. $MD = 2MB$	e. _____

2. **Given:** A, B, and C are collinear.
   $AB = BD$
   $BD = BC$

   Prove: B is the midpoint of $\overline{AC}$.

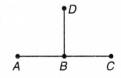

   Proof:

Statements	Reasons
a. A, B, and C are collinear. $AB = BD$ $BD = BC$	a. _____
b. $AB = BC$	b. _____
c. B is the midpoint of $\overline{AC}$.	c. _____

Verifying Segment Relationships

Proofs in geometry follow the same format that you used in Lesson 2–4. The steps in a two-column proof are arranged so that each step follows logically from the preceding one. The reasons can be given information, definitions, postulates of geometry, or rules of algebra. You may also use information that is safe to assume from a given figure.

Example: Write a two-column proof.

Given: $\overline{BC} \cong \overline{DE}$

Prove: $AC = AB + DE$

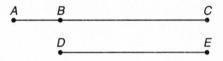

Proof:

Statements	Reasons
a. $\overline{BC} \cong \overline{DE}$	**a.** Given
b. $BC = DE$	**b.** Definition of congruent segments
c. $AC = AB + BC$	**c.** Segment Addition Postulate
d. $AC = AB + BC$	**d.** Substitution Property (=)

Complete each proof by naming the property that justifies each statement.

1. Given: M is the midpoint of $\overline{AB}$.
    B is the midpoint of $\overline{MD}$.

Prove: $MD = 2MB$

Proof:

Statements	Reasons
a. M is the midpoint of $\overline{AB}$. B is the midpoint of $\overline{MD}$.	**a.** Given
b. $AM = MB$ $MB = BD$	**b.** Definition of midpoint
c. $MD = MB + BD$	**c.** Segment Addition Postulate
d. $MD = MB + MB$	**d.** Substitution Property (=)
e. $MD = 2MB$	**e.** Substitution Property (=)

2. Given: A, B, and C are collinear.
    $AB = BD$
    $BD = BC$

Prove: B is the midpoint of $\overline{AC}$.

Proof:

Statements	Reasons
a. A, B, and C are collinear. $AB = BD$ $BD = BC$	**a.** Given
b. $AB = BC$	**b.** Transitive Property (=)
c. B is the midpoint of $\overline{AC}$.	**c.** Definition of midpoint

2-6

Study Guide

Verifying Angle Relationships

Many relationships involving angles can be proved by applying the rules of algebra, as well as the definitions and postulates of geometry.

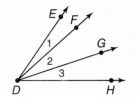

Example: **Given:** $\angle EDG \cong \angle FDH$

Prove: $m\angle 1 = m\angle 3$

Proof:

Statements	Reasons
a. $\angle EDG \cong \angle FDH$	**a.** Given
b. $m\angle EDG = m\angle FDH$	**b.** Definition of congruent angles
c. $m\angle EDG = m\angle 1 + m\angle 2$ $m\angle FDH = m\angle 2 + m\angle 3$	**c.** Angle Addition Postulate
d. $m\angle 1 + m\angle 2 = m\angle 2 + m\angle 3$	**d.** Substitution Property (=)
e. $m\angle 1 = m\angle 3$	**e.** Subtraction Property (=)

Complete the following proofs.

1. Given: $\overline{AB} \perp \overline{BC}$
$m\angle 2 = m\angle 3$

Prove: $m\angle 1 + m\angle 3 = 90$

Proof:

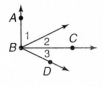

Statements	Reasons
a. $\overline{AB} \perp \overline{BC}$ $m\angle 2 = m\angle 3$	**a.** _____
b. ABC is a right angle.	**b.** _____
c. $m\angle ABC = 90$	**c.** _____
d. $m\angle ABC = m\angle 1 + m\angle 2$	**d.** _____
e. $m\angle 1 + m\angle 2 = 90$	**e.** _____
f. $m\angle 1 + m\angle 3 = 90$	**f.** _____

2. Given: $\angle 1$ and $\angle 2$ form a linear pair.
$m\angle 2 + m\angle 3 + m\angle 4 = 180$

Prove: $m\angle 1 = m\angle 3 + m\angle 4$

Proof:

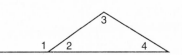

Statements	Reasons
a. $\angle 1$ and $\angle 2$ form a linear pair. $m\angle 2 + m\angle 3 + m\angle 4 = 180$	**a.** _____
b. $\angle 1$ and $\angle 2$ are supplementary.	**b.** _____
c. $m\angle 1 + m\angle 2 = 180$	**c.** _____
d. $m\angle 1 + m\angle 2 =$ $m\angle 2 + m\angle 3 + m\angle 4$	**d.** _____
e. $m\angle 1 = m\angle 3 + m\angle 4$	**e.** _____

NAME_____ DATE _____

Study Guide

Verifying Angle Relationships

Many relationships involving angles can be proved by applying the rules of algebra, as well as the definitions and postulates of geometry.

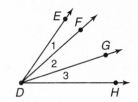

Example: **Given:** $\angle EDG \cong \angle FDH$

Prove: $m\angle 1 = m\angle 3$

Proof:

Statements	Reasons
a. $\angle EDG \cong \angle FDH$	**a.** Given
b. $m\angle EDG = m\angle FDH$	**b.** Definition of congruent angles
c. $m\angle EDG = m\angle 1 + m\angle 2$ $m\angle FDH = m\angle 2 + m\angle 3$	**c.** Angle Addition Postulate
d. $m\angle 1 + m\angle 2 = m\angle 2 + m\angle 3$	**d.** Substitution Property (=)
e. $m\angle 1 = m\angle 3$	**e.** Subtraction Property (=)

Complete the following proofs.

1. **Given:** $\overline{AB} \perp \overline{BC}$
$\qquad\quad m\angle 2 = m\angle 3$

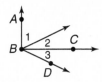

Prove: $m\angle 1 + m\angle 3 = 90$

Proof:

Statements	Reasons
a. $\overline{AB} \perp \overline{BC}$ $m\angle 2 = m\angle 3$	**a.** Given
b. ABC is a right angle.	**b.** Definition of perpendicular lines
c. $m\angle ABC = 90$	**c.** Definition of right angle
d. $m\angle ABC = m\angle 1 + m\angle 2$	**d.** Angle Addition Postulate
e. $m\angle 1 + m\angle 2 = 90$	**e.** Substitution Property (=)
f. $m\angle 1 + m\angle 3 = 90$	**f.** Substitution Property (=)

2. **Given:** $\angle 1$ and $\angle 2$ form a linear pair.
$\qquad\quad m\angle 2 + m\angle 3 + m\angle 4 = 180$

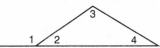

Prove: $m\angle 1 = m\angle 3 + m\angle 4$

Proof:

Statements	Reasons
a. $\angle 1$ and $\angle 2$ form a linear pair. $m\angle 2 + m\angle 3 + m\angle 4 = 180$	**a.** Given
b. $\angle 1$ and $\angle 2$ are supplementary.	**b.** If 2 $\angle$s form a linear pair, they are supp.
c. $m\angle 1 + m\angle 2 = 180$	**c.** Definition of supplementary
d. $m\angle 1 + m\angle 2 =$ $m\angle 2 + m\angle 3 + m\angle 4$	**d.** Substitution Property (=)
e. $m\angle 1 = m\angle 3 + m\angle 4$	**e.** Subtraction Property (=)

Geometry

Study Guide

Parallel Lines and Transversals

When planes do not intersect, they are said to be **parallel**. Also, when lines in the same plane do not intersect, they are parallel. But when lines are not in the same plane and do not intersect, they are **skew**. A line that intersects two or more lines in a plane at different points is called a **transversal**. Eight angles are formed by a transversal and two lines. These angles and pairs of them have special names.

Example: Planes *PQR* and *NOM* are parallel.
Segments *MO* and *RQ* are parallel.
Segments *MN* and *RQ* are skew.

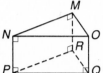

Example: Interior angles: ∠1, ∠2, ∠5, ∠6
Alternate interior angles: ∠1 and ∠6, ∠2 and ∠5
Consecutive interior angles: ∠1 and ∠5, ∠2 and ∠6
Exterior angles: ∠3, ∠4, ∠7, ∠8
Alternate exterior angles: ∠3 and ∠7, ∠4 and ∠8
Corresponding angles: ∠1 and ∠7,
∠2 and ∠8, ∠3 and ∠6, ∠4 and ∠5

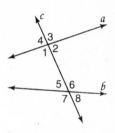

Refer to the figure in the first example.

1. Name two more pairs of parallel segments.

2. Name two more segments skew to $\overline{NM}$.

3. Name two transversals for parallel lines $\overleftrightarrow{NO}$ and $\overleftrightarrow{PQ}$.

4. Name a segment that is parallel to plane *MRQ*.

Identify the special name for each pair of angles in the figure.

5. ∠2 and ∠6

6. ∠4 and ∠8

7. ∠4 and ∠5

8. ∠2 and ∠5

9. Draw a diagram to illustrate two parallel
planes with a line intersecting the planes.

NAME_____ DATE _____

Study Guide

Parallel Lines and Transversals

When planes do not intersect, they are said to be **parallel**. Also, when lines in the same plane do not intersect, they are parallel. But when lines are not in the same plane and do not intersect, they are **skew**. A line that intersects two or more lines in a plane at different points is called a **transversal**. Eight angles are formed by a transversal and two lines. These angles and pairs of them have special names.

Example: Planes *PQR* and *NOM* are parallel.
Segments *MO* and *RQ* are parallel.
Segments *MN* and *RQ* are skew.

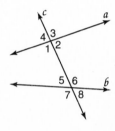

Example: Interior angles: $\angle 1$, $\angle 2$, $\angle 5$, $\angle 6$
Alternate interior angles: $\angle 1$ and $\angle 6$, $\angle 2$ and $\angle 5$
Consecutive interior angles: $\angle 1$ and $\angle 5$, $\angle 2$ and $\angle 6$
Exterior angles: $\angle 3$, $\angle 4$, $\angle 7$, $\angle 8$
Alternate exterior angles: $\angle 3$ and $\angle 7$, $\angle 4$ and $\angle 8$
Corresponding angles: $\angle 1$ and $\angle 7$,
$\angle 2$ and $\angle 8$, $\angle 3$ and $\angle 6$, $\angle 4$ and $\angle 5$

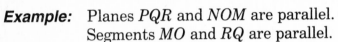

Refer to the figure in the first example.

1. Name two more pairs of parallel segments. **NM and PR, NO and PQ, NP and MR, NP and OQ, MR and OQ**

2. Name two more segments skew to $\overline{NM}$. **PQ, OQ**

3. Name two transversals for parallel lines $\overleftrightarrow{NO}$ and $\overleftrightarrow{PQ}$. **NP, OQ**

4. Name a segment that is parallel to plane *MRQ*. **NP**

Identify the special name for each pair of angles in the figure.

5. $\angle 2$ and $\angle 6$
   consecutive interior angles

6. $\angle 4$ and $\angle 8$
   alternate exterior angles

7. $\angle 4$ and $\angle 5$
   corresponding angles

8. $\angle 2$ and $\angle 5$
   alternate interior angles

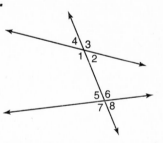

9. Draw a diagram to illustrate two parallel planes with a line intersecting the planes.

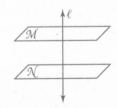

3-2

Study Guide

Angles and Parallel Lines

If two parallel lines are cut by a transversal, then the following pairs of angles are congruent.

corresponding angles   alternate   alternate
                        interior angles   exterior angles

If two parallel lines are cut by a transversal, then consecutive interior angles are supplementary.

Example: In the figure $m \parallel n$ and p is a transversal. If $m\angle 2 = 35$, find the measures of the remaining angles.

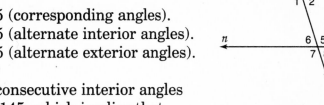

Since $m\angle 2 = 35$, $m\angle 8 = 35$ (corresponding angles).
Since $m\angle 2 = 35$, $m\angle 6 = 35$ (alternate interior angles).
Since $m\angle 8 = 35$, $m\angle 4 = 35$ (alternate exterior angles).

$m\angle 2 + m\angle 5 = 180$. Since consecutive interior angles are supplementary, $m\angle 5 = 145$, which implies that $m\angle 3$, $m\angle 7$, and $m\angle 1$ equal 145.

In the figure at the right $p \parallel q$, $m\angle 1 = 78$, and $m\angle 2 = 47$. Find the measure of each angle.

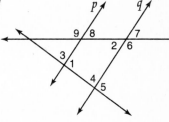

1. $\angle 3$ **2.** $\angle 4$ **3.** $\angle 5$

4. $\angle 6$ **5.** $\angle 7$ **6.** $\angle 8$ **7.** $\angle 9$

Find the values of x and y in each figure.

8.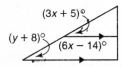

9.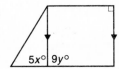

10.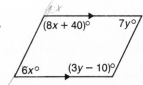

Find the values of x, y and z in each figure.

11.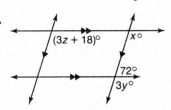

12.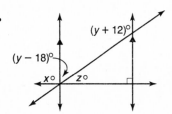

       15   *Geometry*

NAME_____ DATE _____

Study Guide

Angles and Parallel Lines

If two parallel lines are cut by a transversal, then the following pairs of angles are congruent.

corresponding angles   alternate   alternate
                            interior angles   exterior angles

If two parallel lines are cut by a transversal, then consecutive interior angles are supplementary.

Example: In the figure $m \parallel n$ and p is a transversal. If $m\angle 2 = 35$, find the measures of the remaining angles.

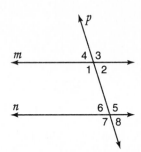

Since $m\angle 2 = 35$, $m\angle 8 = 35$ (corresponding angles).
Since $m\angle 2 = 35$, $m\angle 6 = 35$ (alternate interior angles).
Since $m\angle 8 = 35$, $m\angle 4 = 35$ (alternate exterior angles).

$m\angle 2 + m\angle 5 = 180$. Since consecutive interior angles are supplementary, $m\angle 5 = 145$, which implies that $m\angle 3$, $m\angle 7$, and $m\angle 1$ equal 145.

In the figure at the right $p \parallel q$, $m\angle 1 = 78$, and $m\angle 2 = 47$. Find the measure of each angle.

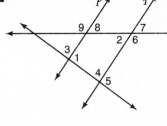

1. $\angle 3$	**2.** $\angle 4$	**3.** $\angle 5$
102	102	78

4. $\angle 6$	**5.** $\angle 7$	**6.** $\angle 8$	**7.** $\angle 9$
133	47	47	133

Find the values of x and y in each figure.

8.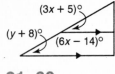

9.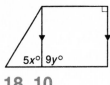

10.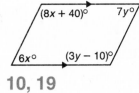

21, 60	18, 10	10, 19

Find the values of x, y and z in each figure.

11.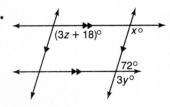

12.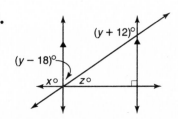

108, 36, 30	90, 93, 15

NAME_____ DATE _____

Study Guide

Integration: Algebra
Slopes of Lines

To find the slope of a line containing two points with coordinates (x_1, y_1) and (x_2, y_2), use the following formula.

$$m = \frac{y_2 - y_1}{x_2 - x_1} \text{ where } x_1 \neq x_2$$

The slope of a vertical line, where $x_1 = x_2$, is undefined.

Two lines have the same slope if and only if they are parallel and nonvertical.

Two nonvertical lines are perpendicular if and only if the product of their slopes is -1.

Example: Find the slope of the line ℓ passing through $A(2, -5)$ and $B(-1, 3)$. State the slope of a line parallel to ℓ. Then state the slope of a line perpendicular to ℓ.

Let $(x_1, y_1) = (2, -5)$ and $(x_2, y_2) = (-1, 3)$.
Then $m = \frac{3 - (-5)}{-1 - 2} = -\frac{8}{3}$.

Any line in the coordinate plane parallel to ℓ has slope $-\frac{8}{3}$.

Since $-\frac{8}{3} \cdot \frac{3}{8} = -1$, the slope of a line perpendicular to the line ℓ is $\frac{3}{8}$.

Find the slope of the line passing through the given points.

1. $C(-2, -4), D(8, 12)$ **2.** $J(-4, 6), K(3, -10)$ **3.** $P(0, 12), R(12, 0)$

4. $S(15, -15), T(-15, 0)$ **5.** $F(21, 12), G(-6, -4)$ **6.** $L(7, 0), M(-17, 10)$

Find the slope of the line parallel to the line passing through each pair of points. Then state the slope of the line perpendicular to the line passing through each pair of points.

7. $I(9, -3), J(6, -10)$ **8.** $G(-8, -12), H(4, -1)$ **9.** $M(5, -2), T(9, -6)$

Study Guide

Integration: Algebra
Slopes of Lines

> To find the slope of a line containing two points with coordinates (x_1, y_1) and (x_2, y_2), use the following formula.
>
> $$m = \frac{y_2 - y_1}{x_2 - x_1} \text{ where } x_1 \neq x_2$$
>
> The slope of a vertical line, where $x_1 = x_2$, is undefined.
>
> Two lines have the same slope if and only if they are parallel and nonvertical.
>
> Two nonvertical lines are perpendicular if and only if the product of their slopes is -1.

Example: Find the slope of the line ℓ passing through $A(2, -5)$ and $B(-1, 3)$. State the slope of a line parallel to ℓ. Then state the slope of a line perpendicular to ℓ.

Let $(x_1, y_1) = (2, -5)$ and $(x_2, y_2) = (-1, 3)$.
Then $m = \frac{3 - (-5)}{-1 - 2} = -\frac{8}{3}$.

Any line in the coordinate plane parallel to ℓ has slope $-\frac{8}{3}$.

Since $-\frac{8}{3} \cdot \frac{3}{8} = -1$, the slope of a line perpendicular to the line ℓ is $\frac{3}{8}$.

Find the slope of the line passing through the given points.

1. $C(-2, -4)$, $D(8, 12)$
$\frac{8}{5}$

2. $J(-4, 6)$, $K(3, -10)$
$-\frac{16}{7}$

3. $P(0, 12)$, $R(12, 0)$
-1

4. $S(15, -15)$, $T(-15, 0)$
$-\frac{1}{2}$

5. $F(21, 12)$, $G(-6, -4)$
$\frac{16}{27}$

6. $L(7, 0)$, $M(-17, 10)$
$-\frac{5}{12}$

Find the slope of the line parallel to the line passing through each pair of points. Then state the slope of the line perpendicular to the line passing through each pair of points.

7. $I(9, -3)$, $J(6, -10)$
$\frac{7}{3}$, $-\frac{3}{7}$

8. $G(-8, -12)$, $H(4, -1)$
$\frac{11}{12}$, $-\frac{12}{11}$

9. $M(5, -2)$, $T(9, -6)$
$-1, 1$

Study Guide

Proving Lines Parallel

Suppose two lines in a plane are cut by a transversal. With enough information about the angles that are formed, you can decide whether the two lines are parallel.

IF	THEN
Corresponding angles are congruent, Alternate interior angles are congruent, Alternate exterior angles are congruent, Consecutive interior angles are supplementary, The lines are perpendicular to the same line,	the lines are parallel.

Example: If $\angle 1 = \angle 2$, which lines must be parallel? Explain.

$\overrightarrow{AC} \parallel \overrightarrow{BD}$ because a pair of corresponding angles are congruent.

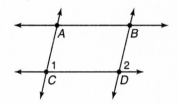

Find the value of x so that $a \parallel b$.

1.

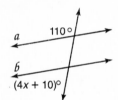

a 110°
b
$(4x + 10)°$

2.

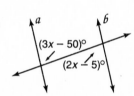

a b
$(3x - 50)°$
$(2x - 5)°$

3.

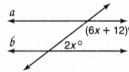

a
b $(6x + 12)°$
$2x°$

4.

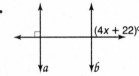

$(4x + 22)°$
a b

5.

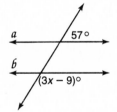

a 57°
b
$(3x - 9)°$

6.

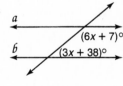

a
b $(6x + 7)°$
$(3x + 38)°$

Given the following information, determine which lines, if any, are parallel. State the postulate or theorem that justifies your answer.

7. $\angle 1 \cong \angle 8$

8. $\angle 4 \cong \angle 9$

9. $m\angle 7 + m\angle 13 = 180$

10. $\angle 9 \cong \angle 13$

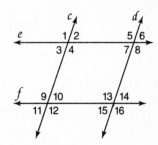

NAME_____ DATE _____

Study Guide

Proving Lines Parallel

Suppose two lines in a plane are cut by a transversal. With enough information about the angles that are formed, you can decide whether the two lines are parallel.

IF	THEN
Corresponding angles are congruent, Alternate interior angles are congruent, Alternate exterior angles are congruent, Consecutive interior angles are supplementary, The lines are perpendicular to the same line,	the lines are parallel.

Example: If ∠1 = ∠2, which lines must be parallel? Explain.

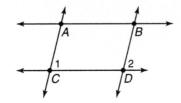

$\overrightarrow{AC} \parallel \overrightarrow{BD}$ because a pair of corresponding angles are congruent.

Find the value of x so that a ∥ b.

1.

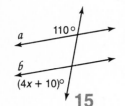

15

2.

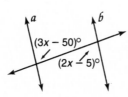

45

3.

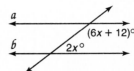

21

4.

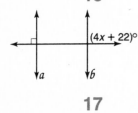

17

5.

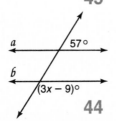

44

6.

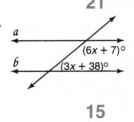

15

Given the following information, determine which lines, if any, are parallel. State the postulate or theorem that justifies your answer.

7. ∠1 ≅ ∠8
c ∥ d, alternate exterior angles congruent

8. ∠4 ≅ ∠9
e ∥ f, alternate interior angles congruent

9. m∠7 + m∠13 = 180
e ∥ f, consecutive interior angles supplementary

10. ∠9 ≅ ∠13
c ∥ d, corresponding angles congruent

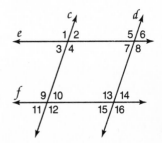

Parallels and Distance

The shortest segment from a point to a line is the perpendicular segment from the point to the line.

Distance Between a Point and a Line	The distance from a line to a point not on the line is the length of the segment perpendicular to the line from the point.
Distance Between Parallel Lines	The distance between two parallel lines is the distance between one of the lines and any point on the other line.

Example 1: Draw the segment that represents the distance indicated.

E to $\overline{AF}$

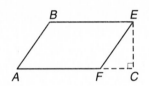

EC represents the distance from E to AF.

Example 2: Use a ruler to determine whether the lines are parallel.

The lines are not everywhere equidistant, therefore they are not parallel.

Draw the segment that represents the distance indicated.

1. K to $\overline{HJ}$

2. A to $\overline{BC}$

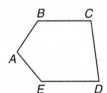

3. T to $\overline{VW}$

4. R to $\overline{NP}$

Use a ruler to determine whether the lines are parallel. Explain your reasoning.

5.

6.

7. Use a ruler to draw a line parallel to the given line through the given point.

Parallels and Distance

The shortest segment from a point to a line is the perpendicular segment from the point to the line.

Distance Between a Point and a Line	The distance from a line to a point not on the line is the length of the segment perpendicular to the line from the point.
Distance Between Parallel Lines	The distance between two parallel lines is the distance between one of the lines and any point on the other line.

Example 1: Draw the segment that represents the distance indicated.

E to $\overline{AF}$

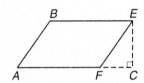

EC represents the distance from E to AF.

Example 2: Use a ruler to determine whether the lines are parallel.

The lines are not everywhere equidistant, therefore they are not parallel.

Draw the segment that represents the distance indicated.

1. K to $\overline{HJ}$

2. A to $\overline{BC}$

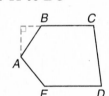

3. T to $\overline{VW}$

4. R to $\overline{NP}$

Use a ruler to determine whether the lines are parallel. Explain your reasoning.

5.

Yes, the lines are 1 cm apart.

6.

No, the lines are not everywhere equidistant.

7. Use a ruler to draw a line parallel to the given line through the given point.

3–6

Study Guide

Integration: Non-Euclidean Geometry
Spherical Geometry

Spherical geometry is one type of **non-Euclidean geometry**. A line is defined as a great circle of a sphere that divides the sphere into two equal half-spheres. A plane is the sphere itself.

Plane Euclidean Geometry Lines on the Plane	Spherical Geometry Great Circles (Lines) on the Sphere
1. A line segment is the shortest path between two points.	1. An arc of a great circle is the shortest path between two points.
2. There is a unique straight line passing through any two points.	2. There is a unique great circle passing through any pair of nonpolar points.
3. A straight line is infinite.	3. A great circle is finite and returns to its original starting point.
4. If three points are collinear, exactly one is between the other two. *A*———•———•———•———*C* *A* *B* *C* *B* is between *A* and *C*.	4. If three points are collinear, any one of the three points is between the other two. *A* is between *B* and *C*. *B* is between *A* and *C*. *C* is between *A* and *B.

Latitude and **longitude**, measured in degrees, are used to locate places on a world map. Latitude provides the locations north or south of the equator. Longitude provides the locations east or west of the prime meridian (0°).

Longitude West

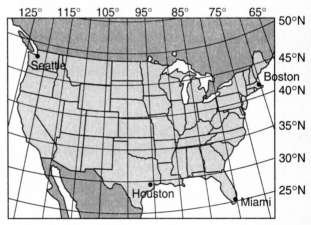

Example: Find a city located near the point with coordinates 29°N and 95°W.

The city near these coordinates is Houston, Texas.

Decide which statements from Euclidean geometry are true in spherical geometry. If false, explain your reasoning.

1. Given a point *Q* and a line *r*, where *Q* is not on *r*, exactly one line perpendicular to *r* passing through *Q* can be drawn.

2. Two lines equidistant from each other are parallel.

Use a globe or world map to name the latitude and longitude of each city.

3. Havana, Cuba   **4.** Beira, Mozambique   **5.** Kabul, Afghanistan

Use a globe or world map to name the city located near each set of coordinates.

6. 39°N, 73°W   **7.** 59°N, 18°E   **8.** 42°S, 146°E

Geometry

Integration: Non-Euclidean Geometry
Spherical Geometry

Spherical geometry is one type of **non-Euclidean geometry**.
A line is defined as a great circle of a sphere that divides the
sphere into two equal half-spheres. A plane is the sphere itself.

Plane Euclidean Geometry Lines on the Plane	Spherical Geometry Great Circles (Lines) on the Sphere
1. A line segment is the shortest path between two points.	1. An arc of a great circle is the shortest path between two points.
2. There is a unique straight line passing through any two points.	2. There is a unique great circle passing through any pair of nonpolar points.
3. A straight line is infinite.	3. A great circle is finite and returns to its original starting point.
4. If three points are collinear, exactly one is between the other two. A⎯⎯B⎯⎯C B is between A and C.	4. If three points are collinear, any one of the three points is between the other two. A is between B and C. B is between A and C. C is between A and B.

Latitude and **longitude**, measured in
degrees, are used to locate places on a
world map. Latitude provides the locations
north or south of the equator. Longitude
provides the locations east or west of the
prime meridian (0°).

Example: Find a city located near the point
with coordinates 29°N and 95°W.

The city near these coordinates is
Houston, Texas.

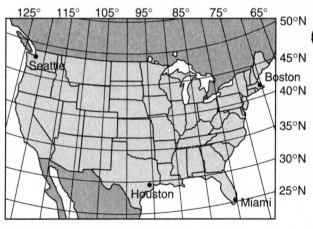

*Decide which statements from Euclidean geometry are true in
spherical geometry. If false, explain your reasoning.*

1. Given a point *Q* and a line *r*, where *Q* is not on *r*, exactly one
   line perpendicular to *r* passing through *Q* can be drawn. **True**

2. Two lines equidistant from each other are parallel. **False;
   there are no parallel lines in spherical geometry.**

Use a globe or world map to name the latitude and longitude of each city.

3. Havana, Cuba
   23°N, 82°W

4. Beira, Mozambique
   18°S, 35°E

5. Kabul, Afghanistan
   35°N, 69°E

Use a globe or world map to name the city located near each set of coordinates.

6. 39°N, 73°W
   New York City, USA

7. 59°N, 18°E
   Stockholm, Sweden

8. 42°S, 146°E
   Hobart, Tasmania

Study Guide

Classifying Triangles

Triangles are classified in two different ways, either by their angles or by their sides.

Classification of Triangles			
Angles		**Sides**	
acute	three acute angles	scalene	no two sides congruent
obtuse	one obtuse angle	isosceles	at least two sides congrent
right	one right angle	equilateral	three sides congruent
equiangular	three congruent angles		

Examples: Classify each triangle by its angles and by its sides.

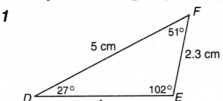

1

△ DEF is obtuse and scalene.   △ MNO is equiangular and equilaterial.

**Use a protractor and ruler to draw triangles using the given
conditions. If possible, classify each triangle by the measures
of its angles and sides.**

1. △ KLM, m∠ K = 90,
KL = 2.5 cm, KM = 3 cm

2. △ XYZ, m∠ X = 60,
XY = YZ = ZX = 3 cm

3. △ DEF, m∠ D = 150,
DE = DF = 1 inch

4. △ GHI, m∠ G = 30,
m∠ H = 45, GH = 4 cm

5. △ NOP, m∠ N = 90,
NO = NP = 2.5 cm

6. △ QRS, m∠ Q = 100,
QS = 1 inch
$QR = 1\frac{1}{2}$ inches

Study Guide

Classifying Triangles

Triangles are classified in two different ways, either by their angles or by their sides.

Classification of Triangles			
Angles		**Sides**	
acute	three acute angles	scalene	no two sides congruent
obtuse	one obtuse angle	isosceles	at least two sides congrent
right	one right angle	equilateral	three sides congruent
equiangular	three congruent angles		

Examples: Classify each triangle by its angles and by its sides.

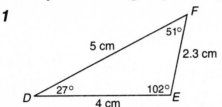

△DEF is obtuse and scalene.   △MNO is equiangular and equilaterial.

Use a protractor and ruler to draw triangles using the given conditions. If possible, classify each triangle by the measures of its angles and sides.

1. △KLM, m∠ K = 90, KL = 2.5 cm, KM = 3 cm

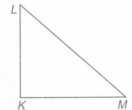

right, scalene

2. △XYZ, m∠ X = 60, XY = YZ = ZX = 3 cm

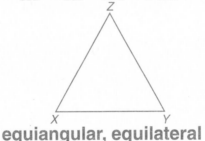

equiangular, equilateral

3. △DEF, m∠ D = 150, DE = DF = 1 inch

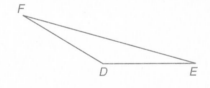

obtuse, isoceles

4. △GHI, m∠ G = 30, m∠ H = 45, GH = 4 cm

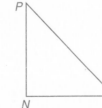

obtuse, scalene

5. △NOP, m∠ N = 90, NO = NP = 2.5 cm

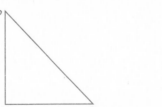

right, isosceles

6. △QRS, m∠ Q = 100, QS = 1 inch, QR = $1\frac{1}{2}$ inches

obtuse, scalene

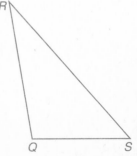

Geometry

Study Guide

Measuring Angles in Triangles

On a separate sheet of paper, draw a triangle of any size. Label the three angles D, E, and F. Then tear off the three corners and rearrange them so that the three vertices meet at one point, with $\angle D$ and $\angle F$ each adjacent to $\angle E$. What do you notice?

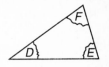

> The sum of the measures of the angles of a triangle is 180.

When one side of a triangle is extended, the angle formed is called the **exterior angle**. In a triangle, the angles not adjacent to an exterior angle are called **remote interior angles**.

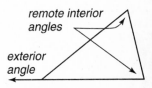

> The measure of an exterior angle of a triangle is equal to the sum of the measures of the two remote interior angles.

Examples: Find the value of x in each figure.

1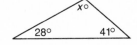

2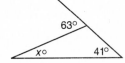

$$28 + 41 + x = 180$$
$$69 + x = 180$$
$$x = 111$$

$$x + 41 = 63$$
$$x = 22$$

Find the value of x.

1.

2.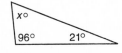

3.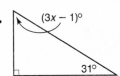

4.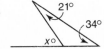

5.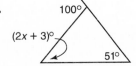

6.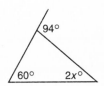

Find the measure of each angle.

7. $\angle 1$

8. $\angle 2$

9. $\angle 3$

10. $\angle 4$

11. $\angle 5$

12. $\angle 6$

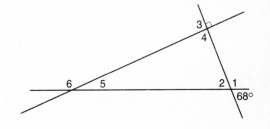

NAME_____ DATE _____

Study Guide

Measuring Angles in Triangles

On a separate sheet of paper, draw a triangle of any size. Label the three angles D, E, and F. Then tear off the three corners and rearrange them so that the three vertices meet at one point, with $\angle D$ and $\angle F$ each adjacent to $\angle E$. What do you notice?

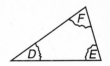

The sum of the measures of the angles of a triangle is 180.

When one side of a triangle is extended, the angle formed is called the **exterior angle**. In a triangle, the angles not adjacent to an exterior angle are called **remote interior angles**.

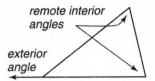

remote interior angles

exterior angle

The measure of an exterior angle of a triangle is equal to the sum of the measures of the two remote interior angles.

Examples: Find the value of x in each figure.

1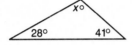

2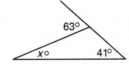

$$28 + 41 + x = 180$$
$$69 + x = 180$$
$$x = 111$$

$$x + 41 = 63$$
$$x = 22$$

Find the value of x.

1.

75

2.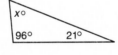

63

3.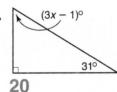

20

4.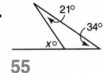

55

5.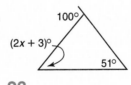

23

6.

17

Find the measure of each angle.

7. $\angle 1$
   112

8. $\angle 2$
   68

9. $\angle 3$
   90

10. $\angle 4$
   90

11. $\angle 5$
   22

12. $\angle 6$
   158

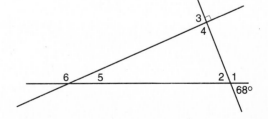

Study Guide

Exploring Congruent Triangles

When two figures have exactly the same shape and size, they are said to be congruent. For two congruent triangles there are three pairs of corresponding (matching) sides and three pairs of corresponding angles. To write a correspondence statement about congruent triangles, you should name corresponding angles in the same order. Remember that congruent parts are marked by identical markings.

Example: Write a correspondence statement for the triangles in the diagram.

$$\triangle LMO \cong \triangle XYZ$$

Complete each correspondence statement.

1.

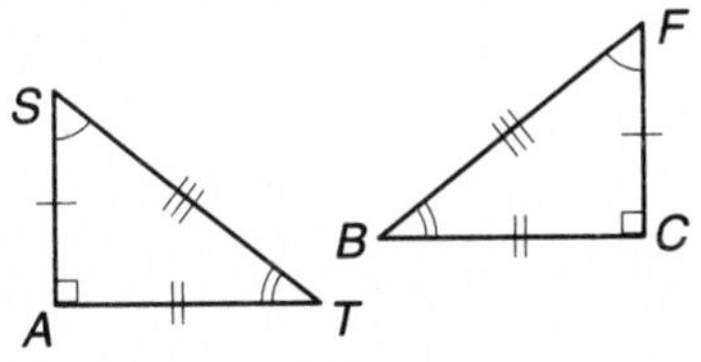

$$\triangle SAT \cong \triangle \underline{?}$$

2.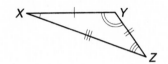

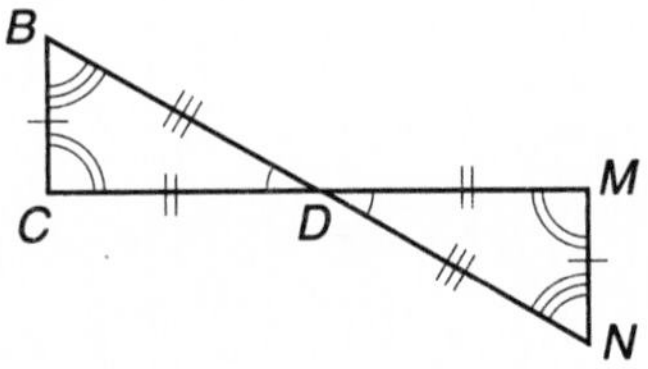

$$\triangle BCD \cong \triangle \underline{?}$$

3.

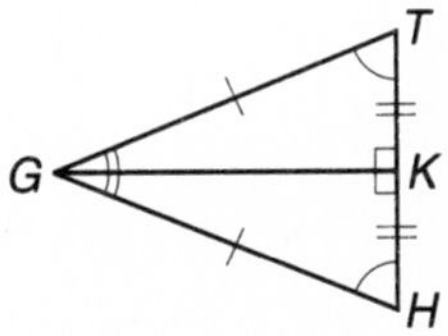

$$\triangle GHK \cong \triangle \underline{?}$$

Write a congruence statement for each pair of congruent triangles.

4.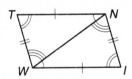

5.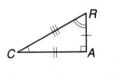

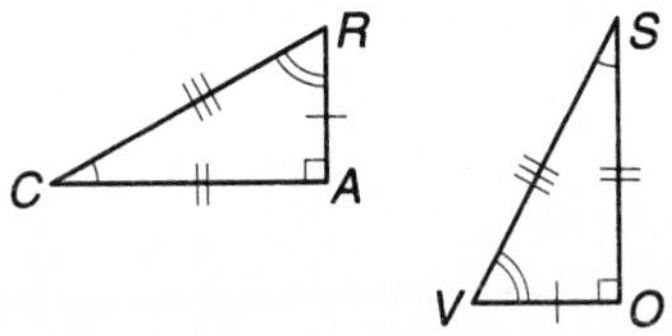

6.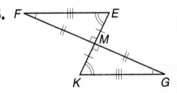

Draw triangles △EDG and △QRS. Label the corresponding parts if △EDG ≅ △QRS. Then complete each statement.

7. $\angle E \cong \underline{?}$

8. $\overline{DG} \cong \underline{?}$

9. $\angle EDG \cong \underline{?}$

10. $\overline{GE} \cong \underline{?}$

11. $\overline{ED} \cong \underline{?}$

12. $\angle EGD \cong \underline{?}$

Study Guide

Exploring Congruent Triangles

When two figures have exactly the same shape and size, they are said to be congruent. For two congruent triangles there are three pairs of corresponding (matching) sides and three pairs of corresponding angles. To write a correspondence statement about congruent triangles, you should name corresponding angles in the same order. Remember that congruent parts are marked by identical markings.

Example: Write a correspondence statement for the triangles in the diagram.

$\triangle LMO \cong \triangle XYZ$

Complete each correspondence statement.

1.	2.	3.
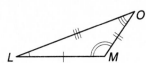	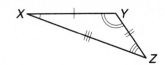	

$\triangle SAT \cong \triangle\,\underline{?}\;$ **FCB** $\triangle BCD \cong \triangle\,\underline{?}\;$ **NMD** $\triangle GHK \cong \triangle\,\underline{?}\;$ **GTK**

Write a congruence statement for each pair of congruent triangles.

4.	5.	6.
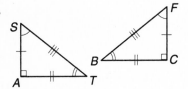	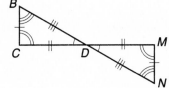	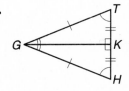

$\triangle TWN \cong \triangle INW$ $\triangle CAR \cong \triangle SOV$ $\triangle FEM \cong \triangle GKM$

Draw triangles $\triangle EDG$ and $\triangle QRS$. Label the corresponding parts if $\triangle EDG \cong \triangle QRS$. Then complete each statement.

7. $\angle E \cong \underline{?}\; \angle Q$ 8. $\overline{DG} \cong \underline{?}\; \overline{RS}$

9. $\angle EDG \cong \underline{?}\; \angle QRS$ 10. $\overline{GE} \cong \underline{?}\; \overline{SQ}$

11. $\overline{ED} \cong \underline{?}\; \overline{QR}$ 12. $\angle EGD \cong \underline{?}\; \angle QSR$

Drawings may vary.

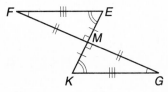

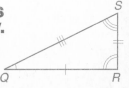

Study Guide

Proving Triangles Congruent

You can show two triangles are congruent with the following:

SSS Postulate (Side–Side–Side)	Three sides of one triangle are congruent to the sides of a second triangle.
SAS Postulate (Side–Angle–Side)	Two sides and the included angle of one triangle are congruent to two sides and an included angle of another triangle.
ASA Postulate (Angle–Side–Angle)	Two angles and the included side of one triangle are congruent to two angles and the included side of another triangle.

Examples: Determine whether each pair of triangles are congruent. If they are congruent, indicate the postulate that can be used to prove their congruence.

1 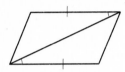   **2** 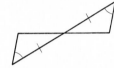   **3**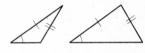

SAS Postulate   ASA Postulate   not congruent

Determine which postulate can be used to prove the triangles are congruent. If it is not possible to prove that they are congruent, write not possible.

1.    **2.** 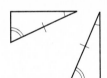   **3.**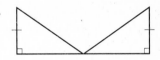

Mark all congruent parts in each figure, complete the prove statement, and identify the postulate that proves their congruence.

4. 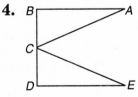   **5.**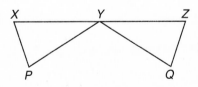

Given: $\angle BCA \cong \angle DCE$
$\angle B$ and $\angle D$ are right angles.
$\overline{BC} \cong \overline{CD}$

Prove: $\triangle CAB \cong$ _____

Given: $\overline{XY} \cong \overline{YZ}$
$\overline{PY} \cong \overline{QY}$
$\overline{XP} \cong \overline{ZQ}$

Prove: $\triangle XYP \cong$ _____

23   *Geometry*

4-4

Study Guide

Proving Triangles Congruent

You can show two triangles are congruent with the following:

SSS Postulate (Side–Side–Side)	Three sides of one triangle are congruent to the sides of a second triangle.
SAS Postulate (Side–Angle–Side)	Two sides and the included angle of one triangle are congruent to two sides and an included angle of another triangle.
ASA Postulate (Angle–Side–Angle)	Two angles and the included side of one triangle are congruent to two angles and the included side of another triangle.

Examples: Determine whether each pair of triangles are congruent. If they are congruent, indicate the postulate that can be used to prove their congruence.

1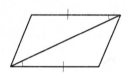

SAS Postulate

2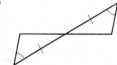

ASA Postulate

3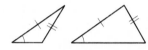

not congruent

Determine which postulate can be used to prove the triangles are congruent. If it is not possible to prove that they are congruent, write _not possible_.

1.

SAS

2.

ASA

3.

not possible

Mark all congruent parts in each figure, complete the prove statement, and identify the postulate that proves their congruence.

4.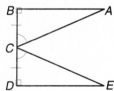

5.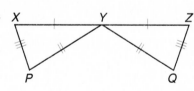

Given: $\angle BCA \cong \angle DCE$
$\angle B$ and $\angle D$ are right angles.
$\overline{BC} \cong \overline{CD}$

Prove: $\triangle CAB \cong \triangle CED$
ASA

Given: $\overline{XY} \cong \overline{YZ}$
$\overline{PY} \cong \overline{QY}$
$\overline{XP} \cong \overline{ZQ}$

Prove: $\triangle XYP \cong \triangle ZYQ$
SSS

Study Guide

Student Edition
Pages 214–221

More Congruent Triangles

In the previous lesson, you learned three postulates for showing that two triangles are congruent: Side–Side–Side (SSS), Side–Angle–Side (SAS), and Angle–Side–Angle (ASA).

Another test for triangle congruence is the Angle–Angle–Side theorem (AAS).

> If two angles and a non-included side of one triangle are congruent to the corresponding two angles and a side of a second triangle, the two triangles are congruent.

Example: In $\triangle ABC$ and $\triangle DBC$, $\overline{AC} \cong \overline{DC}$, and $\angle ACB \cong \angle DCB$. Indicate the additional pair of corresponding parts that would have to be proved congruent in order to use AAS to prove $\triangle ACB \cong \triangle DCB$.

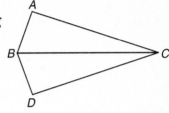

You would need to prove $\angle ABC \cong \angle DBC$ in order to prove that $\triangle ACB \cong \triangle DCB$.

Draw and label triangles ABC and DEF. Indicate the additional pairs of corresponding parts that would have to be proved congruent in order to use the given postulate or theorem to prove the triangles congruent.

1. $\angle B \cong \angle E$ and $\overline{BC} \cong \overline{EF}$ by ASA

2. $\overline{AC} \cong \overline{DF}$ and $\overline{CB} \cong \overline{FE}$ by SSS

Eliminate the possibilities. Determine which postulates show that the triangles are congruent.

3.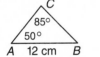

4.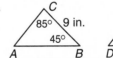

Write a paragraph proof.

5. **Given:** $\overline{HK}$ bisects $\angle GKN$.
$\qquad\angle G \cong \angle N$
Prove: $\overline{GK} \cong \overline{NK}$

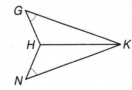

Geometry

NAME_____ DATE _____

Study Guide

Student Edition
Pages 214–221

More Congruent Triangles

In the previous lesson, you learned three postulates for showing that two triangles are congruent: Side–Side–Side (SSS), Side–Angle–Side (SAS), and Angle–Side–Angle (ASA).

Another test for triangle congruence is the Angle–Angle–Side theorem (AAS).

> If two angles and a non-included side of one triangle are congruent to the corresponding two angles and a side of a second triangle, the two triangles are congruent.

Example: In $\triangle ABC$ and $\triangle DBC$, $\overline{AC} \cong \overline{DC}$, and $\angle ACB \cong \angle DCB$. Indicate the additional pair of corresponding parts that would have to be proved congruent in order to use AAS to prove $\triangle ACB \cong \triangle DCB$.

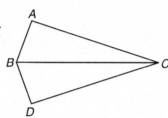

You would need to prove $\angle ABC \cong \angle DBC$ in order to prove that $\triangle ACB \cong \triangle DCB$.

Draw and label triangles ABC and DEF. Indicate the additional pairs of corresponding parts that would have to be proved congruent in order to use the given postulate or theorem to prove the triangles congruent. Drawings will vary.

1. $\angle B \cong \angle E$ and $\overline{BC} \cong \overline{EF}$ by ASA

$\angle C \cong \angle F$

2. $\overline{AC} \cong \overline{DF}$ and $\overline{CB} \cong \overline{FE}$ by SSS

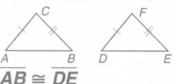

$\overline{AB} \cong \overline{DE}$

Eliminate the possibilities. Determine which postulates show that the triangles are congruent.

3.

AAS

4.

ASA

Write a paragraph proof.

5. Given: $\overline{HK}$ bisects $\angle GKN$.
$\angle G \cong \angle N$
Prove: $\overline{GK} \cong \overline{NK}$

We are given that $\overline{HK}$ bisects $\angle GKN$. So $\angle GKH \cong \angle NKH$. We also are given that $\angle G \cong N$. $\overline{HK} \cong \overline{HK}$ since congruence of segments is reflexive. Therefore, $\triangle GKH \cong \triangle NKH$ by AAS. So, $\overline{GK} \cong \overline{NK}$ by the definition of congruent triangles (CPCTC).

Geometry

Study Guide

Analyzing Isosceles Triangles

Remember that two sides of an isosceles triangle are congruent.
Two important theorems about isosceles triangles are as follows.

If two sides of a triangle are congruent, then the angles opposite those sides are congruent.
If two angles of a triangle are congruent, then the sides opposite those angles are congruent.

Example: Find the value of x.

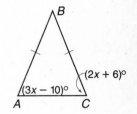

Since $\overline{AB} \cong \overline{BC}$, the angles opposite $\overline{AB}$ and $\overline{BC}$ are congruent. So $m\angle A = m\angle C$.

Therefore, $3x - 10 = 2x + 6$
$$x = 16$$

Find the value of x.

1.

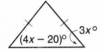

2.

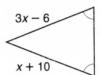

3.

4.

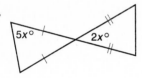

5.

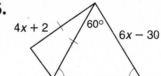

6.

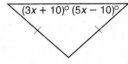

Write a two-column proof.

7. **Given:** $\angle 1 \cong \angle 4$
   Prove: $\overline{DE} \cong \overline{FE}$

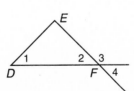

Proof:

Statements	Reasons

Study Guide

Analyzing Isosceles Triangles

Remember that two sides of an isosceles triangle are congruent.
Two important theorems about isosceles triangles are as follows.

If two sides of a triangle are congruent, then the angles opposite those sides are congruent.
If two angles of a triangle are congruent, then the sides opposite those angles are congruent.

Example: Find the value of x.

Since $\overline{AB} \cong \overline{BC}$, the angles opposite $\overline{AB}$ and $\overline{BC}$ are
congruent. So $m\angle A = m\angle C$.

Therefore, $3x - 10 = 2x + 6$
$$x = 16$$

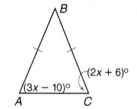

Find the value of x.

1.

20

2.

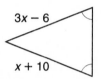

8

3.

76

4.

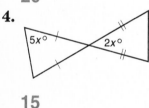

15

5.

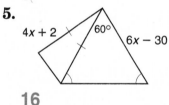

16

6.

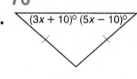

10

Write a two-column proof.

7. Given: $\angle 1 \cong \angle 4$
   Prove: $\overline{DE} \cong \overline{FE}$

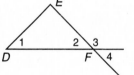

Proof:

Statements	Reasons
a. $\angle 1 \cong \angle 4$	a. Given
b. $\angle 2 \cong \angle 4$	b. Vertical angles are congruent.
c. $\angle 1 \cong \angle 2$	c. Congruence of angles is transitive.
d. $\overline{DE} \cong \overline{FE}$	d. If two angles are congruent, then the sides opposite those angles are congruent.

Geometry

Special Segments in Triangles

Four special types of segments are associated with triangles.

- A **median** is a segment that connects a vertex of a triangle to the midpoint of the opposite side.
- An **altitude** is a segment that has one endpoint at a vertex of a triangle and the other endpoint on the line containing the opposite side so that the altitude is perpendicular to that line.
- An **angle bisector** of a triangle is a segment that bisects an angle of the triangle and has one endpoint at the vertex of that angle and the other endpoint on the side opposite that vertex.
- A **perpendicular bisector** is a segment or line that passes through the midpoint of a side and is perpendicular to that side.

Examples:

1
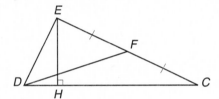

2
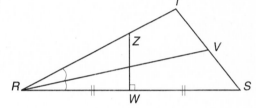

$\overline{DF}$ is a median of $\triangle DEC$.
$\overline{EH}$ is an altitude of $\triangle DEC$.

$\overline{RV}$ is an angle bisector of $\triangle RST$.
$\overline{WZ}$ is a perpendicular bisector of side $\overline{RS}$.

Draw and label a figure to illustrate each situation.

1. $\overline{OQ}$ is a median and an altitude of $\triangle POM$.

2. $\overline{KT}$ is an altitude of $\triangle KLM$, and L is between T and M.

3. $\overline{HS}$ is an angle bisector of $\triangle GHI$, and S is between G and I.

4. $\triangle NRW$ is a right triangle with right angle at N. $\overline{NX}$ is a median of $\triangle NRW$. $\overline{YX}$ is a perpendicular bisector of $\overline{WR}$.

5. $\triangle TRE$ has vertices $T(3, 6)$, $R(-3, 10)$, and $E(-9, 4)$. Find the coordinates of point M if $\overline{TM}$ is a median of $\triangle TRE$.

NAME_____ DATE _____

Study Guide

Special Segments in Triangles

Four special types of segments are associated with triangles.

- A **median** is a segment that connects a vertex of a triangle to the midpoint of the opposite side.
- An **altitude** is a segment that has one endpoint at a vertex of a triangle and the other endpoint on the line containing the opposite side so that the altitude is perpendicular to that line.
- An **angle bisector** of a triangle is a segment that bisects an angle of the triangle and has one endpoint at the vertex of that angle and the other endpoint on the side opposite that vertex.
- A **perpendicular bisector** is a segment or line that passes through the midpoint of a side and is perpendicular to that side.

Examples:

1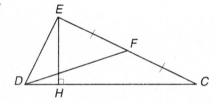

2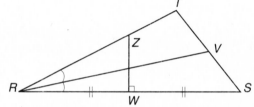

$\overline{DF}$ is a median of $\triangle DEC$.
$\overline{EH}$ is an altitude of $\triangle DEC$.

$\overline{RV}$ is an angle bisector of $\triangle RST$.
$\overline{WZ}$ is a perpendicular bisector of side $\overline{RS}$.

Draw and label a figure to illustrate each situation. Sample answers are given.

1. $\overline{OQ}$ is a median and an altitude of $\triangle POM$.

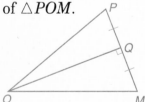

2. $\overline{KT}$ is an altitude of $\triangle KLM$, and L is between T and M.

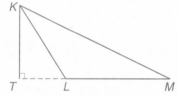

3. $\overline{HS}$ is an angle bisector of $\triangle GHI$, and S is between G and I.

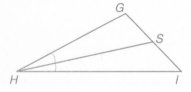

4. $\triangle NRW$ is a right triangle with right angle at N. $\overline{NX}$ is a median of $\triangle NRW$. $\overline{YX}$ is a perpendicular bisector of $\overline{WR}$.

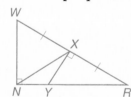

5. $\triangle TRE$ has vertices $T(3, 6)$, $R(-3, 10)$, and $E(-9, 4)$. Find the coordinates of point M if $\overline{TM}$ is a median of $\triangle TRE$. **(−6, 7)**

Geometry

Right Triangles

Two right triangles are congruent if one of the following conditions exist.

Theorem 5-5 LL	If the legs of one right triangle are congruent to the corresponding legs of another right triangle, then the triangles are congruent.
Theorem 5-6 HA	If the hypotenuse and an acute angle of one right triangle are congruent to the hypotenuse and corresponding acute angle of another right triangle, then the two triangles are congruent.
Theorem 5-7 LA	If one leg and an acute angle of one right triangle are congruent to the corresponding leg and acute angle of another right triangle, then the triangles are congruent.
Postulate 5-1 HL	If the hypotenuse and a leg of one right triangle are congruent to the hypotenuse and corresponding leg of another right triangle, then the triangles are congruent.

State the additional information needed to prove each pair of triangles congruent by the given theorem or postulate.

1. HL

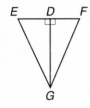

2. HA

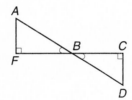

3. LL

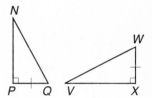

4. LA

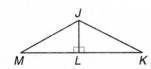

5. HA

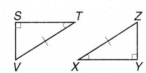

6. LA

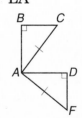

27 *Geometry*

Study Guide

Right Triangles

Two right triangles are congruent if one of the following conditions exist.

Theorem 5-5 LL	If the legs of one right triangle are congruent to the corresponding legs of another right triangle, then the triangles are congruent.
Theorem 5-6 HA	If the hypotenuse and an acute angle of one right triangle are congruent to the hypotenuse and corresponding acute angle of another right triangle, then the two triangles are congruent.
Theorem 5-7 LA	If one leg and an acute angle of one right triangle are congruent to the corresponding leg and acute angle of another right triangle, then the triangles are congruent.
Postulate 5-1 HL	If the hypotenuse and a leg of one right triangle are congruent to the hypotenuse and corresponding leg of another right triangle, then the triangles are congruent.

State the additional information needed to prove each pair of triangles congruent by the given theorem or postulate.

1. HL

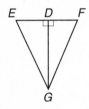

$$\overline{EG} \cong \overline{FG}$$

2. HA

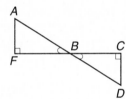

$$\overline{AB} \cong \overline{DB}$$

3. LL

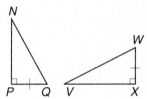

$$\overline{NP} \cong \overline{VX}$$

4. LA

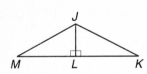

$\angle M \cong \angle K$ or
$\angle MJL \cong \angle KJL$

5. HA

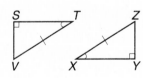

no extra information
needed

6. LA

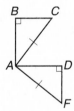

$\overline{BC} \cong \overline{DF}$ or
$\overline{AB} \cong \overline{AD}$, and
$\angle BAC \cong \angle DAF$ or
$\angle C \cong \angle F$

Study Guide

Indirect Proof and Inequalities

A type of proof called **indirect proof** is sometimes used in geometry. In an indirect proof you assume that the conclusion is false and work backward to show that this assumption leads to a contradiction of the original hypothesis or some other known fact, such as a postulate, theorem, or corollary.

The following theorem can be proved by an indirect proof. (See page 253 in your book.)

Exterior Angle Inequality Theorem	If an angle is an exterior angle of a triangle, then its measure is greater than the measure either of its corresponding remote interior angles.

Example: Use the figure at the right to complete the statement with either $<$ or $>$.

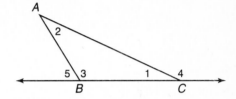

$$m\angle 1 \ \underline{?} \ m\angle 5$$

Since $\angle 5$ is an exterior angle of $\triangle ABC$ and $\angle 1$ and $\angle 2$ are the corresponding remote interior angles, you know that $m\angle 1 < m\angle 5$ by the Exterior Angle Inequality Theorem.

Use the figure at the right to complete each statement with $<$ or $>$.

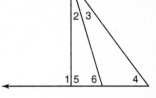

1. $m\angle 1$ _____ $m\angle 6$

2. $m\angle 2$ _____ $m\angle 1$

3. $m\angle 6$ _____ $m\angle 3$

4. $m\angle 4$ _____ $m\angle 6$

5. Use the problem-solving strategy of working backward to complete the indirect proof in paragraph form.
   Given: $m\angle 1 \neq m\angle 2$
   Prove: BD is not an altitude of $\triangle ABC$.

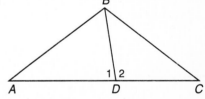

Proof:

a. Assume that _____.

b. Then $\overline{BD} \perp \overline{AC}$ by _____.

c. Since _____,
   $\angle 1$ and $\angle 2$ are right angles.

d. Since all right angles are congruent, _____.

e. Since $\angle 1 \cong \angle 2$, $m\angle 1 =$ _____.

f. But it is given that _____.

g. So our assumption is incorrect. Therefore, _____.

Indirect Proof and Inequalities

A type of proof called **indirect proof** is sometimes used in geometry. In an indirect proof you assume that the conclusion is false and work backward to show that this assumption leads to a contradiction of the original hypothesis or some other known fact, such as a postulate, theorem, or corollary.

The following theorem can be proved by an indirect proof. (See page 253 in your book.)

Exterior Angle Inequality Theorem	If an angle is an exterior angle of a triangle, then its measure is greater than the measure either of its corresponding remote interior angles.

Example: Use the figure at the right to complete the statement with either < or >.

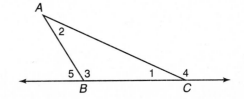

$$m\angle 1 \ \underline{\ ?\ } \ m\angle 5$$

Since $\angle 5$ is an exterior angle of $\triangle ABC$ and $\angle 1$ and $\angle 2$ are the corresponding remote interior angles, you know that $m\angle 1 < m\angle 5$ by the Exterior Angle Inequality Theorem.

Use the figure at the right to complete each statement with < or >.

1. $m\angle 1 \ \underline{\ >\ } \ m\angle 6$

2. $m\angle 2 \ \underline{\ <\ } \ m\angle 1$

3. $m\angle 6 \ \underline{\ >\ } \ m\angle 3$

4. $m\angle 4 \ \underline{\ <\ } \ m\angle 6$

5. Use the problem-solving strategy of working backward to complete the indirect proof in paragraph form.
   Given: $m\angle 1 \neq m\angle 2$
   Prove: BD is not an altitude of $\triangle ABC$.

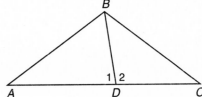

Proof:

a. Assume that <u>$\overline{BD}$ is an altitude of $\triangle ABC$</u>.

b. Then $\overline{BD} \perp \overline{AC}$ by <u>definition of altitude</u>.

c. Since <u>perpendicular segments form four right angles</u>, $\angle 1$ and $\angle 2$ are right angles.

d. Since all right angles are congruent, <u>$\angle 1 \cong \angle 2$</u>.

e. Since $\angle 1 \cong \angle 2$, $m\angle 1 = $ <u>$m\angle 2$</u>.

f. But it is given that <u>$m\angle 1 \neq m\angle 2$</u>.

g. So our assumption is incorrect. Therefore, <u>$\overline{BD}$ is not an altitude of $\triangle ABC$</u>.

5-4

Study Guide

Inequalities for Sides and Angles of a Triangle

Two theorems are very useful for determining relationships between sides and angles of triangles.

- If one side of a triangle is longer than another side, then the angle opposite the longer side is greater than the angle opposite the shorter side.

- If one angle of a triangle is greater than another angle, then the side opposite the greater angle is longer than the side opposite the lesser angle.

Examples: **1** List the angles in order from least to greatest measure.

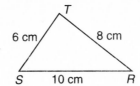

2 List the sides in order from shortest to longest.

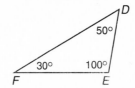

For each triangle, list the angles in order from least to greatest measure.

1.

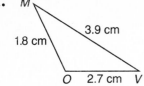

2.

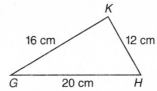

3.

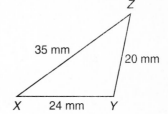

For each triangle, list the sides in order from shortest to longest.

4.

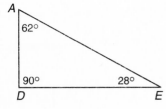

5.

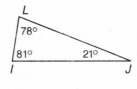

6.

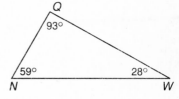

List the sides of △ABC in order from longest to shortest if the angles of △ABC have the indicated measures.

7. $m\angle A = 5x + 2$, $m\angle B = 6x - 10$, $m\angle C = x + 20$

8. $m\angle A = 10x$, $m\angle B = 5x - 17$, $m\angle C = 7x - 1$

Study Guide

Inequalities for Sides and Angles of a Triangle

Two theorems are very useful for determining relationships between sides and angles of triangles.

- If one side of a triangle is longer than another side, then the angle opposite the longer side is greater than the angle opposite the shorter side.

- If one angle of a triangle is greater than another angle, then the side opposite the greater angle is longer than the side opposite the lesser angle.

Examples: **1** List the angles in order from least to greatest measure.   **2** List the sides in order from shortest to longest.

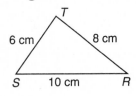

$\angle R, \angle S, \angle T$

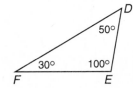

$\overline{DE}, \overline{FE}, \overline{FD}$

For each triangle, list the angles in order from least to greatest measure.

1.

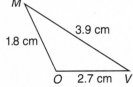

$\angle V, \angle M, \angle O$

2.

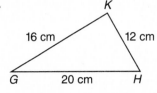

$\angle G, \angle H, \angle K$

3.

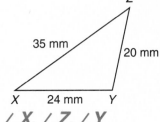

$\angle X, \angle Z, \angle Y$

For each triangle, list the sides in order from shortest to longest.

4.

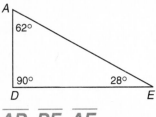

$\overline{AD}, \overline{DE}, \overline{AE}$

5.

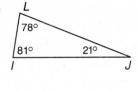

$\overline{IL}, \overline{IJ}, \overline{LJ}$

6.

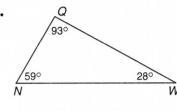

$\overline{NQ}, \overline{QW}, \overline{NW}$

List the sides of △ABC in order from longest to shortest if the angles of △ABC have the indicated measures.

7. $m\angle A = 5x + 2$, $m\angle B = 6x - 10$,
$m\angle C = x + 20$

$\overline{AC}, \overline{BC}, \overline{AB}$

8. $m\angle A = 10x$, $m\angle B = 5x - 17$,
$m\angle C = 7x - 1$

$\overline{BC}, \overline{AB}, \overline{AC}$

Study Guide

The Triangle Inequality

If you take three straws that are 8 inches, 4 inches, and 3 inches in length, can you use these three straws to form a triangle? Without actually trying it, you might think it is possible to form a triangle with the straws. If you try it, however, you will notice that the two smaller straws are too short. This example illustrates the following theorem.

Triangle Inequality Theorem	The sum of the lengths of any two sides of a triangle is greater than the length of the third side.

Example: If the lengths of two sides of a triangle are 7 centimeters and 11 centimeters, between what two numbers must the measure of the third side fall?

Let x = the length of the third side.

By the Triangle Inequality Theorem, each of these inequalities must be true.

$$x + 7 > 11 \qquad\qquad x + 11 > 7 \qquad\qquad 11 + 7 > x$$
$$x > 4 \qquad\qquad\qquad x > {}^-4 \qquad\qquad\qquad 18 > x$$

Therefore, x must be between 4 centimeters and 18 centimeters.

Determine whether it is possible to draw a triangle with sides of the given measures. Write _yes_ or _no_.

1. 15, 12, 9

2. 23, 16, 7

3. 20, 10, 9

4. 8.5, 6.5, 13.5

5. 47, 28, 70

6. 28, 41, 13

The measures of two sides of a triangle are given. Between what two numbers must the measure of the third side fall?

7. 9 and 15

8. 11 and 20

9. 23 and 14

10. Suppose you have three different positive numbers arranged in order from greatest to least. Which sum is it most crucial to test to see if the numbers could be the lengths of the sides of a triangle?

Geometry

Study Guide

The Triangle Inequality

If you take three straws that are 8 inches, 4 inches, and 3 inches
in length, can you use these three straws to form a triangle?
Without actually trying it, you might think it is possible to form
a triangle with the straws. If you try it, however, you will notice
that the two smaller straws are too short. This example
illustrates the following theorem.

Triangle Inequality Theorem	The sum of the lengths of any two sides of a triangle is greater than the length of the third side.

Example: If the lengths of two sides of a triangle are
7 centimeters and 11 centimeters, between what two
numbers must the measure of the third side fall?

Let x = the length of the third side.

By the Triangle Inequality Theorem, each of these
inequalities must be true.

$$x + 7 > 11 \qquad x + 11 > 7 \qquad 11 + 7 > x$$
$$x > 4 \qquad\qquad x > {}^-4 \qquad\qquad 18 > x$$

Therefore, x must be between 4 centimeters and 18
centimeters.

**Determine whether it is possible to draw a triangle with sides
of the given measures. Write _yes_ or _no_.**

1. 15, 12, 9 **yes**

2. 23, 16, 7 **no**

3. 20, 10, 9 **no**

4. 8.5, 6.5, 13.5 **yes**

5. 47, 28, 70 **yes**

6. 28, 41, 13 **no**

**The measures of two sides of a triangle are given. Between
what two numbers must the measure of the third side fall?**

7. 9 and 15 **6 and 24**

8. 11 and 20 **9 and 31**

9. 23 and 14 **9 and 37**

10. Suppose you have three different positive numbers arranged in order
from greatest to least. Which sum is it most crucial to test to see if the
numbers could be the lengths of the sides of a triangle? **the sum of
the two smaller numbers**

5-6

Study Guide

Inequalities Involving Two Triangles

The following two theorems are useful in determining relationships between sides and angles in triangles.

SAS Inequality (Hinge Theorem)	If two sides of one triangle are congruent to two sides of another triangle, and the included angle in one triangle is greater than the included angle in the other, then the third side of the first triangle is longer than the third side in the second triangle.
SSS Inequality	If two sides of one triangle are congruent to two sides of another triangle and the third side in one triangle is longer than the third side in the other, then the angle between the pair of congruent sides in the first triangle is greater than the corresponding angle in the second triangle.

Examples: Refer to each figure to write an inequality relating the given pair of angle or segment measures.

1 $m\angle 1, m\angle 2$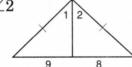

2 AD, BE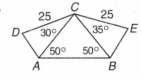

By SSS, $m\angle 1 > m\angle 2$. By SAS, $AD < BE$.

Refer to each figure to write an inequality relating the given pair of angle or segment measures.

1. UT, TS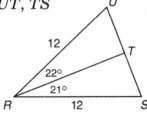

2. $m\angle LPM, m\angle MPN$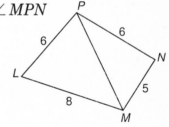

3. $m\angle 1, m\angle 2$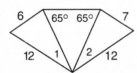

4. $m\angle KPE, m\angle GPH$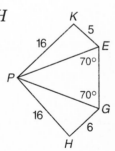

Write an inequality or pair of inequalities to describe the possible values of x.

5.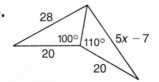

6.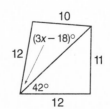

Study Guide

Student Edition
Pages 273–279

Inequalities Involving Two Triangles

The following two theorems are useful in determining relationships between sides and angles in triangles.

SAS Inequality (Hinge Theorem)	If two sides of one triangle are congruent to two sides of another triangle, and the included angle in one triangle is greater than the included angle in the other, then the third side of the first triangle is longer than the third side in the second triangle.
SSS Inequality	If two sides of one triangle are congruent to two sides of another triangle and the third side in one triangle is longer than the third side in the other, then the angle between the pair of congruent sides in the first triangle is greater than the corresponding angle in the second triangle.

Examples: Refer to each figure to write an inequality relating the given pair of angle or segment measures.

1 $m\angle 1, m\angle 2$

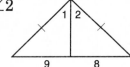

By SSS, $m\angle 1 > m\angle 2$.

2 AD, BE

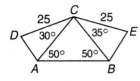

By SAS, $AD < BE$.

Refer to each figure to write an inequality relating the given pair of angle or segment measures.

1. UT, TS

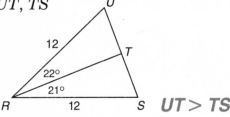

$UT > TS$

2. $m\angle LPM, m\angle MPN$

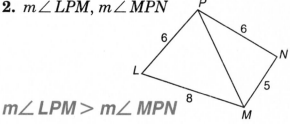

$m\angle LPM > m\angle MPN$

3. $m\angle 1, m\angle 2$

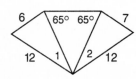

$m\angle 1 < m\angle 2$

4. $m\angle KPE, m\angle GPH$

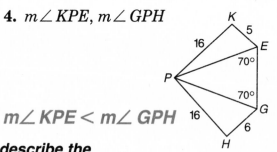

$m\angle KPE < m\angle GPH$

Write an inequality or pair of inequalities to describe the possible values of x.

5.

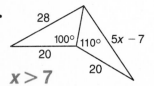

$x > 7$

6.

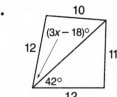

$6 < x$ and $x < 20$

Study Guide

Parallelograms

Any four-sided polygon is called a **quadrilateral**. A segment joining any two nonconsecutive vertices in a quadrilateral is called a **diagonal**. A special kind of quadrilateral in which both pairs of opposite sides are parallel is called a **parallelogram**.

The following theorems all concern parallelograms.

- Opposite sides of a parallelogram are congruent.
- Opposite angles of a parallelogram are congruent.
- Consecutive angles in a parallelogram are supplementary.
- The diagonals of a parallelogram bisect each other.

Example: If the quadrilateral in the figure is a parallelogram, find the values of x, y, and z.

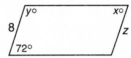

Since opposite angles of a parallelogram are congruent, $x = 72$.

Since consecutive angles of a parallelogram are supplementary, $y + 72 = 180$. Therefore, $y = 108$.

Since opposite sides of a parallelogram are congruent, $z = 8$.

If each quadrilateral is a parallelogram, find the values of x, y, and z.

1.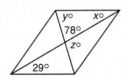

2.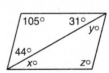

3.

4. In parallelogram $ABCD$, $m \angle A = 3x$ and $m \angle B = 4x + 40$. Find the measure of angles A, B, C, and D.

5. In parallelogram $RSTV$, diagonals $\overline{RT}$ and $\overline{VS}$ intersect at Q. If $RQ = 5x + 1$ and $QT = 3x + 15$, find QT.

Explain why it is impossible for each figure to be a parallelogram.

6.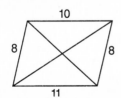

7.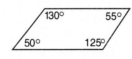

Geometry

NAME_____ DATE _____

Study Guide

Parallelograms

Any four-sided polygon is called a **quadrilateral**. A segment joining any two nonconsecutive vertices in a quadrilateral is called a **diagonal**. A special kind of quadrilateral in which both pairs of opposite sides are parallel is called a **parallelogram**.

The following theorems all concern parallelograms.

- Opposite sides of a parallelogram are congruent.
- Opposite angles of a parallelogram are congruent.
- Consecutive angles in a parallelogram are supplementary.
- The diagonals of a parallelogram bisect each other.

Example: If the quadrilateral in the figure is a parallelogram, find the values of x, y, and z.

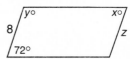

Since opposite angles of a parallelogram are congruent, $x = 72$.

Since consecutive angles of a parallelogram are supplementary, $y + 72 = 180$. Therefore, $y = 108$.

Since opposite sides of a parallelogram are congruent, $z = 8$.

If each quadrilateral is a parallelogram, find the values of x, y, and z.

1.

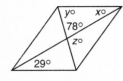

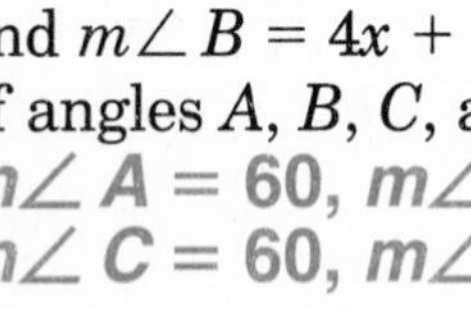

29, 73, 102

2.

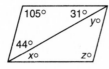

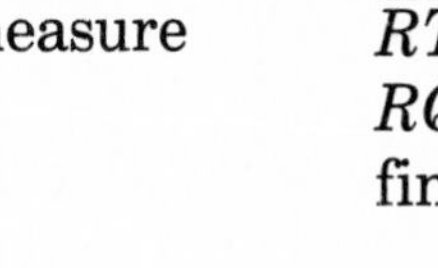

31, 44, 105

3.

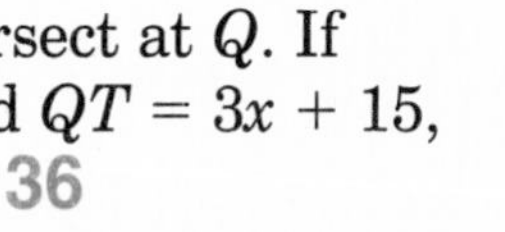

73, 73, 107

4. In parallelogram $ABCD$, $m\angle A = 3x$ and $m\angle B = 4x + 40$. Find the measure of angles A, B, C, and D.
$m\angle A = 60$, $m\angle B = 120$,
$m\angle C = 60$, $m\angle D = 120$

5. In parallelogram $RSTV$, diagonals $\overline{RT}$ and $\overline{VS}$ intersect at Q. If $RQ = 5x + 1$ and $QT = 3x + 15$, find QT. $QT = 36$

Explain why it is impossible for each figure to be a parallelogram.

6.

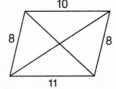

Each pair of opposite sides should be congruent.

7.

The opposite angles should be congruent.

Geometry

6-2

Study Guide

Tests for Parallelograms

You can show that a quadrilateral is a parallelogram if you can show that one of the following is true.

1. Both pairs of opposite sides are parallel.

2. Both pairs of opposite sides are congruent.

3. Diagonals bisect each other.

4. Both pairs of opposite angles are congruent.

5. A pair of opposite sides are both parallel and congruent.

Example: Find the values of x and y that ensure the quadrilateral is a parallelogram.

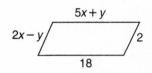

Since opposite sides of a parallelogram must be congruent, then $5x + y = 18$ and $5x - y = 2$.

Solving the system of two equations, you get $x = 2$ and $y = 8$.

Determine if each quadrilateral is a parallelogram. Justify your answer.

1.

2.
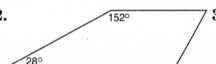

3.

Find the values of x and y that ensure each quadrilateral is a parallelogram.

4.
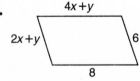

5.
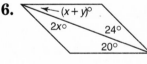

6.
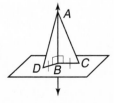

7. Identify the subgoals you would need to accomplish to complete the proof.

   Given: $\overleftrightarrow{AB} \perp$ plane BCD.
   $\overline{DB} \cong \overline{CB}$

   Prove: $\angle DAB \cong \angle CAB$

Tests for Parallelograms

You can show that a quadrilateral is a parallelogram if you can show that one of the following is true.

1. Both pairs of opposite sides are parallel.
2. Both pairs of opposite sides are congruent.
3. Diagonals bisect each other.
4. Both pairs of opposite angles are congruent.
5. A pair of opposite sides are both parallel and congruent.

Example: Find the values of x and y that ensure the quadrilateral is a parallelogram.

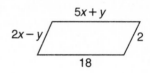

Since opposite sides of a parallelogram must be congruent, then $5x + y = 18$ and $5x - y = 2$.

Solving the system of two equations, you get $x = 2$ and $y = 8$.

Determine if each quadrilateral is a parallelogram. Justify your answer.

1.

2.

3.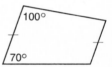

Yes; both pairs of opposite sides are congruent.

No; the top and bottom sides are parallel, but the other pair may not be.

No; top and bottom sides are not parallel.

Find the values of x and y that ensure each quadrilateral is a parallelogram.

4.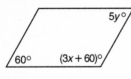

5.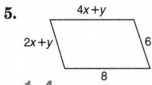

6.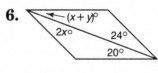

20, 12

1, 4

12, 8

7. Identify the subgoals you would need to accomplish to complete the proof.

Given: $\overleftrightarrow{AB} \perp$ plane BCD.
$\overline{DB} \cong \overline{CB}$

Prove: $\angle DAB \cong \angle CAB$
Prove $\triangle ADB \cong \triangle ACB$, then show $\angle DAB \cong \angle CAB$.

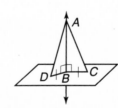

Study Guide

Rectangles

A **rectangle** is a quadrilateral with four right angles. Since both pairs of opposite angles are congruent, a rectangle is a parallelogram and has all the properties of a parallelogram. The following list summarizes the properties of a rectangle.

- Opposite sides are congruent.
- Opposite angles are congruent.
- Consecutive angles are supplementary.
- Diagonals bisect each other.
- All four angles are right angles.
- Diagonals are congruent.

Example: Quadrilateral $EFGH$ is a rectangle. If $EM = 5x + 1$ and $HF = 42$, find the value of x.

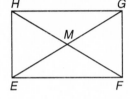

Since the diagonals of a rectangle bisect each other and are congruent, you know that $5x + 1 = \frac{1}{2}(42)$.

$$5x + 1 = 21$$
$$5x = 20$$
$$x = 4$$

Quadrilateral RSTV is a rectangle. Find the values of x and y.

1. $VW = 2x + y$
   $WS = 36$
   $RS = x - y$
   $VT = 9$

2. $VR = y$
   $TS = x + 11$
   $VT = y - 3x$
   $RS = x + 2$

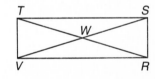

Quadrilateral ABCD is a rectangle. Find the value of x.

3. $m\angle DAC = 4x + 8$
   $m\angle CAB = 5x - 8$

4. $AC = x^2$
   $DB = 6x - 8$

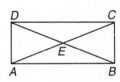

Determine whether ABCD is a rectangle. Justify your answer.

5. $A(10, 4), B(10, 8),$
   $C(-4, 8), D(-4, 4)$

6. $A(3, 7), B(10, 7),$
   $C(11, 12), D(4, 12)$

Study Guide

Student Edition
Pages 306-312

Rectangles

A **rectangle** is a quadrilateral with four right angles. Since both pairs of opposite angles are congruent, a rectangle is a parallelogram and has all the properties of a parallelogram. The following list summarizes the properties of a rectangle.

- Opposite sides are congruent.
- Opposite angles are congruent.
- Consecutive angles are supplementary.
- Diagonals bisect each other.
- All four angles are right angles.
- Diagonals are congruent.

Example: Quadrilateral $EFGH$ is a rectangle. If $EM = 5x + 1$ and $HF = 42$, find the value of x.

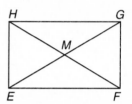

Since the diagonals of a rectangle bisect each other and are congruent, you know that $5x + 1 = \frac{1}{2}(42)$.

$$5x + 1 = 21$$
$$5x = 20$$
$$x = 4$$

Quadrilateral RSTV is a rectangle. Find the values of x and y.

1. $VW = 2x + y$
   $WS = 36$
   $RS = x - y$
   $VT = 9$ **15, 6**

2. $VR = y$
   $TS = x + 11$
   $VT = y - 3x$
   $RS = x + 2$ **3, 14**

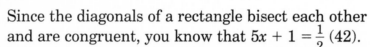

Quadrilateral ABCD is a rectangle. Find the value of x.

3. $m\angle DAC = 4x + 8$
   $m\angle CAB = 5x - 8$ **10**

4. $AC = x^2$
   $DB = 6x - 8$ **2 or 4**

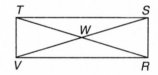

Determine whether ABCD is a rectangle. Justify your answer.

5. $A(10, 4)$, $B(10, 8)$,
   $C(-4, 8)$, $D(-4, 4)$
   Yes; opposite sides are parallel and all angles are right angles.

6. $A(3, 7)$, $B(10, 7)$,
   $C(11, 12)$, $D(4, 12)$
   no; not all right angles

6-4

Study Guide

Squares and Rhombi

A **rhombus** is a quadrilateral with four congruent sides. A **square** is a quadrilateral with four right angles and four congruent sides.

The diagonals of a rhombus have two special relationships.

* The diagonals of a rhombus are perpendicular.
* Each diagonal of a rhombus bisects a pair of opposite angles.

Example: $ABCD$ is a rhombus. If $m\angle ADB = 27$, find $m\angle ADC$.

Since each diagonal of a rhombus bisects a pair of opposite angles, $m\angle ADC = 2(m\angle ADB)$. So $m\angle ADC = 2(27)$ or 54.

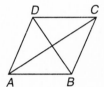

Use rhombus PQRS and the given information to find each value.

1. If $ST = 13$, find SQ.

2. If $m\angle PRS = 17$, find $m\angle QRS$.

3. Find $m\angle STR$.

4. If $SP = 4x - 3$ and $PQ = 18 + x$, find the value of x.

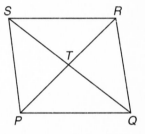

Determine whether each quadrilateral with the given vertices is a parallelogram, a rectangle, a rhombus, or a square. List all that apply.

5. $M(1, 5)$, $N(6, 5)$, $O(6, 10)$, $P(1, 10)$

6. $W(-4, -2)$, $X(5, -2)$, $Y(8, 4)$, $Z(-1, 4)$

7. $D(-7, 3)$, $E(-2, 3)$, $F(1, 7)$, $G(-4, 7)$

8. $R(0, 0)$, $E(10, 0)$, $S(10, 5)$, $T(0, 5)$

Study Guide

Squares and Rhombi

A **rhombus** is a quadrilateral with four congruent sides. A **square** is a quadrilateral with four right angles and four congruent sides.

The diagonals of a rhombus have two special relationships.

- The diagonals of a rhombus are perpendicular.
- Each diagonal of a rhombus bisects a pair of opposite angles.

Example: $ABCD$ is a rhombus. If $m\angle ADB = 27$, find $m\angle ADC$.

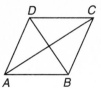

Since each diagonal of a rhombus bisects a pair of opposite angles, $m\angle ADC = 2(m\angle ADB)$. So $m\angle ADC = 2(27)$ or 54.

Use rhombus PQRS and the given information to find each value.

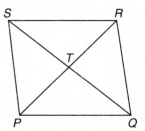

1. If $ST = 13$, find SQ. **26**

2. If $m\angle PRS = 17$, find $m\angle QRS$. **34**

3. Find $m\angle STR$. **90**

4. If $SP = 4x - 3$ and $PQ = 18 + x$, find the value of x. **7**

Determine whether each quadrilateral with the given vertices is a parallelogram, a rectangle, a rhombus, or a square. List all that apply.

5. $M(1, 5)$, $N(6, 5)$, $O(6, 10)$, $P(1, 10)$
parallelogram, rectangle, rhombus, square

6. $W(-4, -2)$, $X(5, -2)$, $Y(8, 4)$, $Z(-1, 4)$
parallelogram

7. $D(-7, 3)$, $E(-2, 3)$, $F(1, 7)$, $G(-4, 7)$
parallelogram, rhombus

8. $R(0, 0)$, $E(10, 0)$, $S(10, 5)$, $T(0, 5)$
parallelogram, rectangle

Trapezoids

A **trapezoid** is a quadrilateral with exactly one pair of parallel sides. The parallel sides are called **bases**, and the nonparallel sides are called **legs**. In trapezoid *EFGH*, $\angle E$ and $\angle F$ are called **base angles**. $\angle H$ and $\angle G$ form the other pair of base angles.

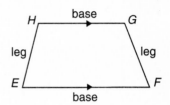

A trapezoid is an **isosceles trapezoid** if its legs are congruent.

The **median** of a trapezoid is the segment that joins the midpoints of the legs.

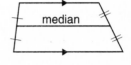

The following theorems about trapezoids can be proved.

- Both pairs of base angles of an isosceles trapezoid are congruent.
- The diagonals of an isosceles trapezoid are congruent.
- The median of a trapezoid is parallel to the bases, and its measure is one-half the sum of the measures of the bases.

Example: Given trapezoid *RSTV* with median $\overline{MN}$, find the value of *x*.

$MN = \frac{1}{2}(VT + RS)$

$15 = \frac{1}{2}(6x - 3 + 8x + 5)$

$15 = \frac{1}{2}(14x + 2)$

$15 = 7x + 1$

$14 = 7x$

$2 = x$

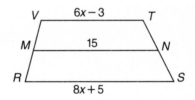

HJKL is an isosceles trapezoid with bases $\overline{HJ}$ and $\overline{LK}$, and median RS. Use the given information to solve each problem.

1. If *LK* = 30 and *HJ* = 42, find *RS*.

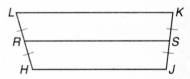

2. If *RS* = 17 and *HJ* = 14, find *LK*.

3. If *RS* = *x* + 5 and *HJ* + *LK* = 4*x* + 6, find *RS*.

4. If $m\angle LRS = 66$, find $m\angle KSR$.

5. Find the length of the median of a trapezoid with vertices at *C*(3, 1), *D*(10, 1), *E*(7, 9), and *F*(5, 9).

Study Guide

Trapezoids

A **trapezoid** is a quadrilateral with exactly one pair of parallel sides. The parallel sides are called **bases**, and the nonparallel sides are called **legs**. In trapezoid $EFGH$, $\angle E$ and $\angle F$ are called **base angles**. $\angle H$ and $\angle G$ form the other pair of base angles.

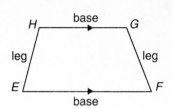

A trapezoid is an **isosceles trapezoid** if its legs are congruent.

The **median** of a trapezoid is the segment that joins the midpoints of the legs.

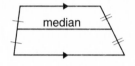

The following theorems about trapezoids can be proved.

- Both pairs of base angles of an isosceles trapezoid are congruent.
- The diagonals of an isosceles trapezoid are congruent.
- The median of a trapezoid is parallel to the bases, and its measure is one-half the sum of the measures of the bases.

Example: Given trapezoid $RSTV$ with median $\overline{MN}$, find the value of x.

$MN = \frac{1}{2}(VT + RS)$

$15 = \frac{1}{2}(6x - 3 + 8x + 5)$

$15 = \frac{1}{2}(14x + 2)$

$15 = 7x + 1$

$14 = 7x$

$2 = x$

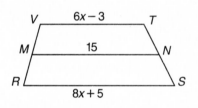

HJKL is an isosceles trapezoid with bases $\overline{HJ}$ and $\overline{LK}$, and median RS. Use the given information to solve each problem.

1. If $LK = 30$ and $HJ = 42$, find RS. **36**

2. If $RS = 17$ and $HJ = 14$, find LK. **20**

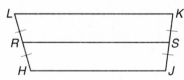

3. If $RS = x + 5$ and $HJ + LK = 4x + 6$, find RS. **7**

4. If $m\angle LRS = 66$, find $m\angle KSR$. **66**

5. Find the length of the median of a trapezoid with vertices at $C(3, 1)$, $D(10, 1)$, $E(7, 9)$, and $F(5, 9)$. $\frac{9}{2}$

7–1

Study Guide

Integration: Algebra
Using Proportions

A **ratio** is a comparison of two quantities. The ratio of a to b can be expressed as $\frac{a}{b}$, where b is not 0. The ratio can also be written $a{:}b$.

An equation stating that two ratios are equal is a **proportion**. Therefore, $\frac{a}{b} = \frac{c}{d}$ is a proportion for any numbers a and c and any nonzero numbers b and d. In any true proportion, the cross products are equal. So, $\frac{a}{b} = \frac{c}{d}$ if and only if $ad = bc$.

Example: Solve $\frac{11}{16} = \frac{44}{x}$ by using cross products.

$$\frac{11}{16} = \frac{44}{x}$$
$$11x = 16 \cdot 44$$
$$11x = 704$$
$$x = 64$$

For Exercises 1–4, use the table to find the ratios. Express each ratio as a decimal rounded to three places.

Teams	Wins	Losses
Hawks	16	13
Tigers	15	14
Mustangs	12	16

1. games won to games lost for Hawks

2. games won by the Hawks to games won by Tigers

3. games won to games played for Tigers

4. games won to games played for Mustangs

Solve each proportion by using cross products.

5. $\dfrac{9}{28} = \dfrac{x}{84}$

6. $\dfrac{3}{18} = \dfrac{4x}{7}$

7. $\dfrac{x+5}{7} = \dfrac{x+3}{5}$

Use a proportion to solve each problem.

8. If two cassettes cost $14.50, how much will 15 cassettes cost?

9. If a 6-foot post casts a shadow that is 8 feet long, how tall is an antenna that casts a 60-foot shadow at the same time?

NAME_____ DATE _____

Study Guide

Integration: Algebra
Using Proportions

A **ratio** is a comparison of two quantities. The ratio of a to b can be expressed as $\frac{a}{b}$, where b is not 0. The ratio can also be written $a{:}b$.

An equation stating that two ratios are equal is a **proportion**. Therefore, $\frac{a}{b} = \frac{c}{d}$ is a proportion for any numbers a and c and any nonzero numbers b and d. In any true proportion, the cross products are equal. So, $\frac{a}{b} = \frac{c}{d}$ if and only if $ad = bc$.

Example: Solve $\frac{11}{16} = \frac{44}{x}$ by using cross products.

$$\frac{11}{16} = \frac{44}{x}$$
$$11x = 16 \cdot 44$$
$$11x = 704$$
$$x = 64$$

For Exercises 1–4, use the table to find the ratios. Express each ratio as a decimal rounded to three places.

Teams	Wins	Losses
Hawks	16	13
Tigers	15	14
Mustangs	12	16

1. games won to games lost for Hawks **1.231**

2. games won by the Hawks to games won by Tigers **1.067**

3. games won to games played for Tigers **0.517**

4. games won to games played for Mustangs **0.429**

Solve each proportion by using cross products.

5. $\frac{9}{28} = \frac{x}{84}$ **27**

6. $\frac{3}{18} = \frac{4x}{7}$ **$\frac{7}{24}$**

7. $\frac{x+5}{7} = \frac{x+3}{5}$ **2**

Use a proportion to solve each problem.

8. If two cassettes cost $14.50, how much will 15 cassettes cost? **$108.75**

9. If a 6-foot post casts a shadow that is 8 feet long, how tall is an antenna that casts a 60-foot shadow at the same time? **45 ft**

Study Guide

Exploring Similar Polygons

Two polygons are **similar** if and only if their corresponding angles are congruent and the measures of their corresponding sides are proportional.

The symbol ~ means *is similar to*.

The ratio of the lengths of two corresponding sides of two similar polygons is called the **scale factor**.

Example: Find x if $\triangle RST \sim \triangle XYZ$.

The corresponding sides are proportional, so we can write a proportion to find the value of x.

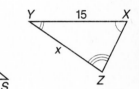

$$\frac{16}{x} = \frac{20}{15}$$
$$20x = 240$$
$$x = 12$$

If quadrilateral ABCD is similar to quadrilateral EFGH, find each of the following.

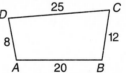
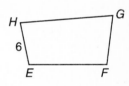

1. scale factor of $ABCD$ to $EFGH$

2. EF

3. FG

4. GH

5. perimeter of $ABCD$

6. perimeter of $EFGH$

7. ratio of perimeter of $ABCD$ to perimeter of $EFGH$

Each pair of polygons is similar. Find the values of x and y.

8.

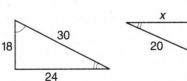

9.

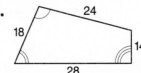
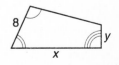

Study Guide

Exploring Similar Polygons

Two polygons are **similar** if and only if their corresponding angles are congruent and the measures of their corresponding sides are proportional.

The symbol ~ means *is similar to*.

The ratio of the lengths of two corresponding sides of two similar polygons is called the **scale factor**.

Example: Find x if $\triangle RST \sim \triangle XYZ$.

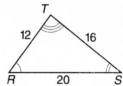 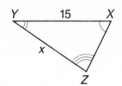

The corresponding sides are proportional, so we can write a proportion to find the value of x.

$$\frac{16}{x} = \frac{20}{15}$$
$$20x = 240$$
$$x = 12$$

If quadrilateral ABCD is similar to quadrilateral EFGH, find each of the following.

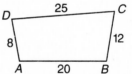

1. scale factor of $ABCD$ to $EFGH$ $\frac{4}{3}$

2. EF **15**

3. FG **9**

4. GH $18\frac{3}{4}$

5. perimeter of $ABCD$ **65**

6. perimeter of $EFGH$ $48\frac{3}{4}$

7. ratio of perimeter of $ABCD$ to perimeter of $EFGH$ $\frac{4}{3}$

Each pair of polygons is similar. Find the values of x and y.

8.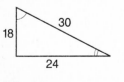

16, 12

9.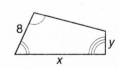

$12\frac{4}{9}, 6\frac{2}{9}$

NAME_____ DATE _____

Study Guide

Identifying Similar Triangles

There are three ways to determine whether two triangles are similar.

- Show that two angles of one triangle are congruent to two angles of the other triangle. (AA Similarity)

- Show that the measures of the corresponding sides of the triangles are proportional. (SSS Similarity)

- Show that the measure of two sides of a triangle are proportional to the measures of the corresponding sides of the other triangle and that the included angles are congruent. (SAS Similarity)

Example: Determine whether the triangles are similar. Explain your answer.

Since $\frac{15}{12} = \frac{25}{20} = \frac{20}{16}$, the triangles are similar by SSS Similarity.

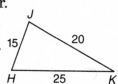
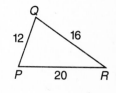

Determine whether each pair of triangles is similar. Give a reason for your answer.

1.
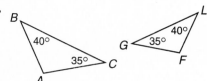

2.
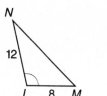

3.
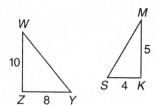

4.
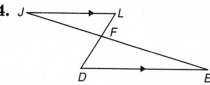

Identify the similar triangles in each figure. Explain why they are similar and find the missing measures.

5. If $\overline{MN} \parallel \overline{AB}$, find AB, BC, and BN.

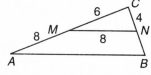

6. If $MNPQ$ is a parallelogram, find RN, RP, and SP.

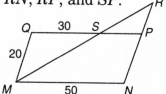

Geometry

Study Guide

Identifying Similar Triangles

There are three ways to determine whether two triangles are similar.

- Show that two angles of one triangle are congruent to two angles of the other triangle. (AA Similarity)

- Show that the measures of the corresponding sides of the triangles are proportional. (SSS Similarity)

- Show that the measure of two sides of a triangle are proportional to the measures of the corresponding sides of the other triangle and that the included angles are congruent. (SAS Similarity)

Example: Determine whether the triangles are similar. Explain your answer.

Since $\frac{15}{12} = \frac{25}{20} = \frac{20}{16}$, the triangles are similar by SSS Similarity.

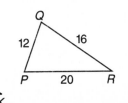

Determine whether each pair of triangles is similar. Give a reason for your answer.

1.

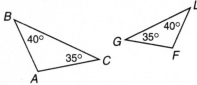

yes; AA

2.

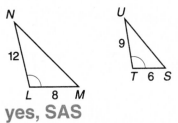

yes, SAS

3.

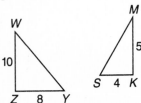

no; no information on angles

4.

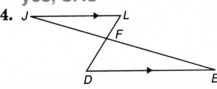

yes, AA

Identify the similar triangles in each figure. Explain why they are similar and find the missing measures.

5. If $\overline{MN} \parallel \overline{AB}$, find AB, BC, and BN.

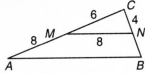

$\triangle CMN \sim \triangle CAB$; AA;
$18\frac{2}{3}, 9\frac{1}{3}, 5\frac{1}{3}$

6. If $MNPQ$ is a parallelogram, find RN, RP, and SP.

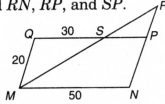

$\triangle QSM \sim \triangle PSR \sim \triangle NMR$; AA;
$33\frac{1}{3}, 13\frac{1}{3}, 20$

Study Guide

Parallel Lines and Proportional Parts

The following theorems involve proportional parts of triangles.

- If a line is parallel to one side of a triangle and intersects the other two sides, then it separates these sides into segments of proportional lengths.

- If a line intersects two sides of a triangle and separates the sides into corresponding segments of proportional lengths, then the line is parallel to the third side.

- A segment whose endpoints are the midpoints of two sides of a triangle is parallel to the third side of the triangle and its length is one-half the length of the third side.

Example: In $\triangle ABC$, $\overline{EF} \parallel \overline{CB}$, find the value of x.

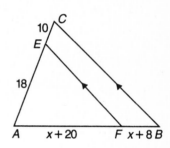

$\overline{EF} \parallel \overline{CB}$ implies that $\dfrac{AF}{FB} = \dfrac{AE}{EC}$.

Rewrite the proportion and solve.

$$\frac{x + 20}{x + 8} = \frac{18}{10}$$
$$10x + 200 = 18x + 144$$
$$56 = 8x$$
$$7 = x$$

Find the value of x.

1.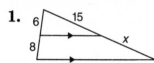

2.

3.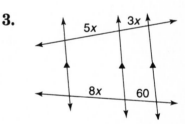

In $\triangle ABC$, find x so that $\overline{DE} \parallel \overline{CB}$.

4. $DC = 18$, $AD = 6$,
$AE = 12$, $EB = x - 3$

5. $AC = 30$, $AD = 10$,
$AE = 22$, $EB = x + 4$

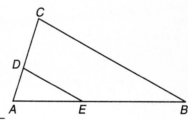

6. In $\triangle RST$, M is the midpoint of $\overline{RS}$, N is the midpoint of $\overline{ST}$, and P is the midpoint of $\overline{RT}$. Find the perimeter of $\triangle MNP$ if $RS = 28$, $ST = 34$, and $RT = 30$.

Study Guide

Parallel Lines and Proportional Parts

The following theorems involve proportional parts of triangles.

- If a line is parallel to one side of a triangle and intersects the other two sides, then it separates these sides into segments of proportional lengths.

- If a line intersects two sides of a triangle and separates the sides into corresponding segments of proportional lengths, then the line is parallel to the third side.

- A segment whose endpoints are the midpoints of two sides of a triangle is parallel to the third side of the triangle and its length is one-half the length of the third side.

Example: In $\triangle ABC$, $\overline{EF} \parallel \overline{CB}$, find the value of x.

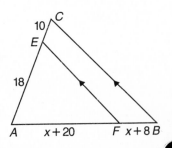

$\overline{EF} \parallel \overline{CB}$ implies that $\dfrac{AF}{FB} = \dfrac{AE}{EC}$.

Rewrite the proportion and solve.

$$\frac{x + 20}{x + 8} = \frac{18}{10}$$
$$10x + 200 = 18x + 144$$
$$56 = 8x$$
$$7 = x$$

Find the value of x.

1.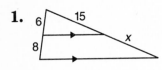

20

2.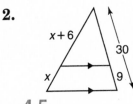

4.5

3.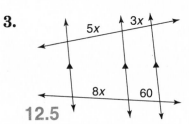

12.5

In △ABC, find x so that $\overline{DE} \parallel \overline{CB}$.

4. $DC = 18$, $AD = 6$,
$AE = 12$, $EB = x - 3$
39

5. $AC = 30$, $AD = 10$,
$AE = 22$, $EB = x + 4$
40

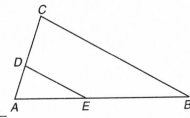

6. In $\triangle RST$, M is the midpoint of $\overline{RS}$, N is the midpoint of $\overline{ST}$, and P is the midpoint of $\overline{RT}$. Find the perimeter of $\triangle MNP$ if $RS = 28$, $ST = 34$, and $RT = 30$. **46**

NAME_____ DATE _____

Study Guide

Parts of Similar Triangles

Each mathematical word in the following list has a different meaning in everyday usage than when it is used in a mathematical context. When you read mathematics, you must be sure that you are using each word in the correct context.

altitude	right	mean	scale
extreme	product	segment	ruler
plane	obtuse	acute	
meter	yard	median	

Each definition below describes an everyday usage of one of the words in the list above. For each definition, write the correct word from the list above in the blanks at the right.

1. an instrument for measuring _____

2. a tool for smoothing a wood surface _____

3. the opposite of left _____

4. differing widely from the ordinary _____

5. keen in perception _____

6. dull _____

7. contemptible _____

8. fragment _____

9. the dividing strip down the middle of a highway _____

10. height above sea level _____

11. a person in charge of a country _____

12. the grounds of a building _____

13. an item that is manufactured _____

14. a small plate forming part of the external covering of a fish _____

15. Choose five words from the list above. Compare their mathematical definition and their everyday usage. Describe how the definitions are similar and how they are different.

Study Guide

Parts of Similar Triangles

Each mathematical word in the following list has a different meaning in everyday usage than when it is used in a mathematical context. When you read mathematics, you must be sure that you are using each word in the correct context.

altitude	right	mean	scale
extreme	product	segment	ruler
plane	obtuse	acute	
meter	yard	median	

Each definition below describes an everyday usage of one of the words in the list above. For each definition, write the correct word from the list above in the blanks at the right.

1. an instrument for measuring _meter_

2. a tool for smoothing a wood surface _plane_

3. the opposite of left _right_

4. differing widely from the ordinary _extreme_

5. keen in perception _acute_

6. dull _obtuse_

7. contemptible _mean_

8. fragment _segment_

9. the dividing strip down the middle of a highway _median_

10. height above sea level _altitude_

11. a person in charge of a country _ruler_

12. the grounds of a building _yard_

13. an item that is manufactured _product_

14. a small plate forming part of the external covering of a fish _scale_

15. Choose five words from the list above. Compare their mathematical definition and their everyday usage. Describe how the definitions are similar and how they are different.
    See students' work.

Study Guide

Fractals and Self-Similarity

Fractal geometry is the geometry of things in nature that are irregular in shape. A **fractal** is a geometric shape created using a process called **iteration**. Iteration is a process of repeating the same procedure over and over again. **Self-similarity** is a characteristic of fractals. The smaller and smaller details of a shape have the same geometrical characteristics as the original, larger form.

Example:

Stage 1   Stage 2   Stage 3

1. Follow the iteration process to produce a figure.

   • Draw a square.
   • Attach the hypotenuse of an isosceles right triangle to one side of the square. The hypotenuse should be the same length as the side of the square.
   • Attach a square to each leg of the triangle. The sides of the squares should be the same length as the legs of the triangle.

   This is Stage 1.

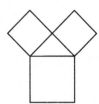

2. Describe the next step in the iteration process.

3. Draw Stage 3 of the figure in Exercise 1.

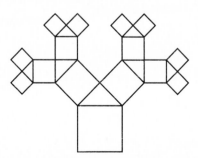

4. Is the figure produced in Exercise 3 self-similar?

Fractals and Self-Similarity

Fractal geometry is the geometry of things in nature that are irregular in shape. A **fractal** is a geometric shape created using a process called **iteration**. Iteration is a process of repeating the same procedure over and over again. **Self-similarity** is a characteristic of fractals. The smaller and smaller details of a shape have the same geometrical characteristics as the original, larger form.

Example:

Stage 1

Stage 2

Stage 3

1. Follow the iteration process to produce a figure.

   • Draw a square.
   • Attach the hypotenuse of an isosceles right triangle to one side of the square. The hypotenuse should be the same length as the side of the square.
   • Attach a square to each leg of the triangle. The sides of the squares should be the same length as the legs of the triangle.

   This is Stage 1.

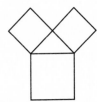

2. Describe the next step in the iteration process.
   Attach an isosceles right triangle to each of the two smaller squares.

3. Draw Stage 3 of the figure in Exercise 1.

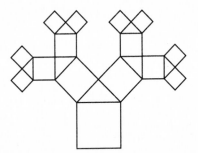

4. Is the figure produced in Exercise 3 self-similar? **Yes**

8–1

Study Guide

Geometric Mean and the Pythagorean Theorem

The geometric mean between two positive numbers a and b is the positive number x where $\frac{a}{x} = \frac{x}{b}$.

If $\triangle ABC$ is a right triangle with altitude $\overline{BD}$, then the following relationships hold true.

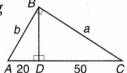

$$\frac{AD}{BD} = \frac{BD}{DC} \qquad \frac{AD}{BC} = \frac{BC}{DC} \qquad \frac{AC}{AB} = \frac{AB}{AD}$$

You can use the Pythagorean Theorem to find missing measures for right triangles.

Pythagorean Theorem	In a right triangle, the sum of the squares of the measures of the legs equals the square of the measure of the hypotenuse.
Converse of the Pythagorean Theorem	If the sum of the squares of the measures of two sides of a triangle equals the square of the measure of the longest side, then the triangle is a right triangle.

Use $\triangle ABC$ above for the following examples.

Examples: **1** Find a.
You can use geometric mean relationships.
$$\frac{AD}{BC} = \frac{BC}{DC}$$
$$\frac{20}{a} = \frac{a}{50}$$
$$a^2 = 1000$$
$$a = \sqrt{1000}$$
$$a \approx 31.6$$

2 Find b.
You can use the Pythagorean Theorem.
$$b^2 + a^2 = 70^2$$
$$b^2 + 1000 = 4900$$
$$b^2 = 3900$$
$$b = \sqrt{3900}$$
$$b \approx 62.4$$

Find the geometric mean between each pair of numbers.

1. 3 and 10

2. 10 and 20

3. 10 and 40

Find the values of x and y. Round to the nearest tenth.

4.

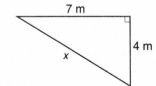

5.

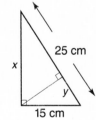

6.

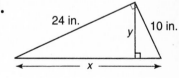

Determine if the given measures are measures of the sides of a right triangle.

7. 18, 24, 30

8. 20, 30, 40

9. 4.5, 6, 7.5

NAME_____ DATE _____

Study Guide

Geometric Mean and the Pythagorean Theorem

The geometric mean between two positive numbers a and b is the positive number x where $\frac{a}{x} = \frac{x}{b}$.

If $\triangle ABC$ is a right triangle with altitude $\overline{BD}$, then the following relationships hold true.

$$\frac{AD}{BD} = \frac{BD}{DC} \qquad \frac{AD}{BC} = \frac{BC}{DC} \qquad \frac{AC}{AB} = \frac{AB}{AD}$$

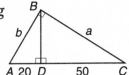

You can use the Pythagorean Theorem to find missing measures for right triangles.

Pythagorean Theorem	In a right triangle, the sum of the squares of the measures of the legs equals the square of the measure of the hypotenuse.
Converse of the Pythagorean Theorem	If the sum of the squares of the measures of two sides of a triangle equals the square of the measure of the longest side, then the triangle is a right triangle.

Use $\triangle ABC$ above for the following examples.

Examples:

1 Find a.
You can use geometric mean relationships.
$$\frac{AD}{BC} = \frac{BC}{DC}$$
$$\frac{20}{a} = \frac{a}{50}$$
$$a^2 = 1000$$
$$a = \sqrt{1000}$$
$$a \approx 31.6$$

2 Find b.
You can use the Pythagorean Theorem.
$$b^2 + a^2 = 70^2$$
$$b^2 + 1000 = 4900$$
$$b^2 = 3900$$
$$b = \sqrt{3900}$$
$$b \approx 62.4$$

Find the geometric mean between each pair of numbers.

1. 3 and 10 $\sqrt{30} \approx 5.5$ **2.** 10 and 20 $\sqrt{200} \approx 14.1$ **3.** 10 and 40 **20**

Find the values of x and y. Round to the nearest tenth.

4.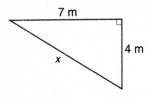

8.1 m

5.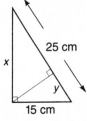

20 cm, 9 cm

6.

26 in., 9.2 in.

Determine if the given measures are measures of the sides of a right triangle.

7. 18, 24, 30 **yes**   **8.** 20, 30, 40 **no**   **9.** 4.5, 6, 7.5 **yes**

Study Guide

Special Right Triangles

Two special kinds of right triangles are the 45°-45°-90° triangle and the 30°-60°-90° right triangle.

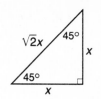

- In a 45°-45°-90° triangle, the hypotenuse is $\sqrt{2}$ times as long as a leg.
- In a 30°-60°-90° triangle, the hypotenuse is twice as long as the shorter leg and the longer leg is $\sqrt{3}$ times as long as the shorter leg.

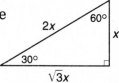

Examples: Find the value of x.

1

Since the triangle is a 45°-45°-90° triangle, the hypotenuse is $\sqrt{2}$ times as long as the leg.

So $x = 5\sqrt{2}$ or about 7.1.

2

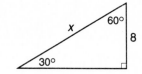

Since the triangle is a 30°-60°-90° triangle, the hypotenuse is twice as long as the shorter leg.

So $x = 2(8)$ or 16.

Find the value of x.

1.

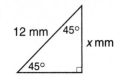

2.

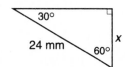

3.

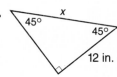

4.

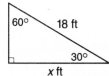

5.

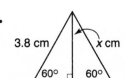

6.

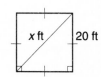

7. Find the perimeter of the triangle shown at the right.

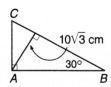

Study Guide

Special Right Triangles

Two special kinds of right triangles are the 45°-45°-90° triangle and the 30°-60°-90° right triangle.

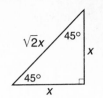

- In a 45°-45°-90° triangle, the hypotenuse is $\sqrt{2}$ times as long as a leg.
- In a 30°-60°-90° triangle, the hypotenuse is twice as long as the shorter leg and the longer leg is $\sqrt{3}$ times as long as the shorter leg.

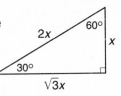

Examples: Find the value of x.

1

Since the triangle is a 45°-45°-90° triangle, the hypotenuse is $\sqrt{2}$ times as long as the leg.

So $x = 5\sqrt{2}$ or about 7.1.

2

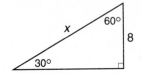

Since the triangle is a 30°-60°-90° triangle, the hypotenuse is twice as long as the shorter leg.

So $x = 2(8)$ or 16.

Find the value of x.

1.

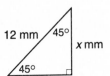

$6\sqrt{2} \approx 8.5$ mm

2.

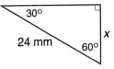

12 mm

3.

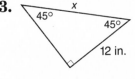

$12\sqrt{2} \approx 17.0$ in.

4.

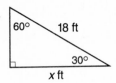

$9\sqrt{3} \approx 15.6$ ft

5.

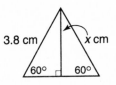

$1.9\sqrt{3} \approx 3.3$ cm

6.

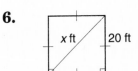

$20\sqrt{2} \approx 28.3$ ft

7. Find the perimeter of the triangle shown at the right.
$40 + 20 + 20\sqrt{3} \approx 94.6$ *cm*

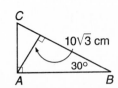

Study Guide

Integration: Trigonometry
Ratios in Right Triangles

A ratio of the lengths of two sides of a right triangle is called a **trigonometric ratio**. The three most common ratios are **sine**, **cosine**, and **tangent**. Their abbreviations are *sin*, *cos*, and *tan*, respectively. These ratios are defined for the acute angles of right triangles, though your calculator will give the values of sine, cosine, and tangent for angles of greater measure.

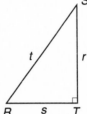

$$\sin R = \frac{\text{leg opposite} \angle R}{\text{hypotenuse}} = \frac{r}{t}$$

$$\cos R = \frac{\text{leg adjacent to} \angle R}{\text{hypotenuse}} = \frac{s}{t}$$

$$\tan R = \frac{\text{leg opposite to} \angle R}{\text{leg adjacent to} \angle R} = \frac{r}{s}$$

Example: Find sin D, cos D, and tan D. Express each ratio as a fraction and as a decimal rounded to the nearest thousandth.

$$\sin D = \frac{5}{13} \approx 0.385$$

$$\cos D = \frac{12}{13} \approx 0.923$$

$$\tan D = \frac{5}{12} \approx 0.417$$

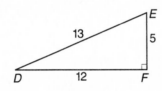

Find the indicated trigonometric ratio as a fraction and as a decimal rounded to the nearest ten-thousandth.

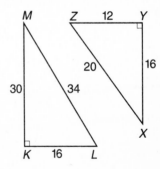

1. sin M

2. cos Z

3. tan L

4. sin X

5. cos L

6. tan Z

Find the value of each ratio to the nearest ten-thousandth.

7. sin 12°

8. cos 32°

9. tan 74°

10. sin 55°

Study Guide

Integration: Trigonometry
Ratios in Right Triangles

A ratio of the lengths of two sides of a right triangle is called a
trigonometric ratio. The three most common ratios are **sine**,
cosine, and **tangent**. Their abbreviations are *sin*, *cos*, and *tan*,
respectively. These ratios are defined for the acute angles of right
triangles, though your calculator will give the values of sine,
cosine, and tangent for angles of greater measure.

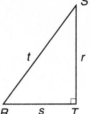

$$\sin R = \frac{\text{leg opposite } \angle R}{\text{hypotenuse}} = \frac{r}{t}$$

$$\cos R = \frac{\text{leg adjacent to } \angle R}{\text{hypotenuse}} = \frac{s}{t}$$

$$\tan R = \frac{\text{leg opposite to } \angle R}{\text{leg adjacent to } \angle R} = \frac{r}{s}$$

Example: Find sin D, cos D, and tan D. Express each ratio as a
fraction and as a decimal rounded to the nearest
thousandth.

$$\sin D = \frac{5}{13} \approx 0.385$$

$$\cos D = \frac{12}{13} \approx 0.923$$

$$\tan D = \frac{5}{12} \approx 0.417$$

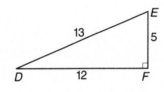

**Find the indicated trigonometric ratio as a fraction and as a
decimal rounded to the nearest ten-thousandth.**

1. sin M $\frac{8}{17} \approx$ **0.4706**

2. cos Z $\frac{3}{5} \approx$ **0.6000**

3. tan L $\frac{15}{8} \approx$ **1.8750**

4. sin X $\frac{3}{5} \approx$ **0.6000**

5. cos L $\frac{8}{17} \approx$ **0.4706**

6. tan Z $\frac{4}{3} \approx$ **1.3333**

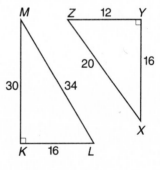

Find the value of each ratio to the nearest ten-thousandth.

7. sin 12° **0.2079**

8. cos 32° **0.8480**

9. tan 74° **3.4874**

10. sin 55° **0.8192**

Study Guide

Angles of Elevation and Depression

Many problems in daily life can be solved by using trigonometry. Often such problems involve an **angle of elevation** or an **angle of depression**.

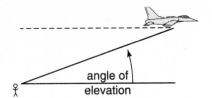

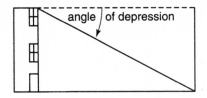

Example: The angle of elevation from point A to the top of a cliff is 38°. If point A is 80 feet from the base of the cliff, how high is the cliff?

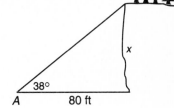

Let x represent the height of the cliff.
Then $\tan 38° = \frac{x}{80}$.

$80 \tan 38° = x$

Use a calculator set for the degree mode to find x.

ENTER: 80 ⊠ 38 TAN ⊟ 62.502850

The cliff is about 63 feet high.

Solve each problem. Round measures of segments to the nearest hundredth and measures of angles to the nearest degree.

1. From the top of a tower, the angle of depression to a stake on the ground is 72°. The top of the tower is 80 feet above ground. How far is the stake from the foot of the tower?

2. A tree 40 feet high casts a shadow 58 feet long. Find the measure of the angle of elevation of the sun.

3. A ladder leaning against a house makes an angle of 60° with the ground. The foot of the ladder is 7 feet from the foundation of the house. How long is the ladder?

4. A balloon on a 40-foot string makes an angle of 50° with the ground. How high above the ground is the balloon if the hand of the person holding the balloon is 6 feet above the ground?

Study Guide

Angles of Elevation and Depression

Many problems in daily life can be solved by using trigonometry. Often such problems involve an **angle of elevation** or an **angle of depression**.

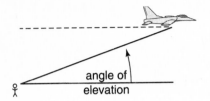

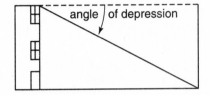

Example: The angle of elevation from point A to the top of a cliff is 38°. If point A is 80 feet from the base of the cliff, how high is the cliff?

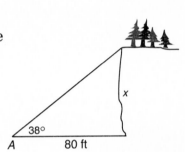

Let x represent the height of the cliff.
Then $\tan 38° = \dfrac{x}{80}$.

$80 \tan 38° = x$

Use a calculator set for the degree mode to find x.

ENTER: 80 ⊠ 38 [TAN] ⊟ 62.502850

The cliff is about 63 feet high.

Solve each problem. Round measures of segments to the nearest hundredth and measures of angles to the nearest degree.

1. From the top of a tower, the angle of depression to a stake on the ground is 72°. The top of the tower is 80 feet above ground. How far is the stake from the foot of the tower? **25.99 ft**

2. A tree 40 feet high casts a shadow 58 feet long. Find the measure of the angle of elevation of the sun. **35°**

3. A ladder leaning against a house makes an angle of 60° with the ground. The foot of the ladder is 7 feet from the foundation of the house. How long is the ladder? **14 ft**

4. A balloon on a 40-foot string makes an angle of 50° with the ground. How high above the ground is the balloon if the hand of the person holding the balloon is 6 feet above the ground? **36.64 ft**

Study Guide

Using the Law of Sines

Trigonometric functions can also be used to solve problems that involve triangles that are not right triangles.

Law of Sines	Let $\triangle ABC$ be any triangle with a, b, and c representing the measures of sides opposite angles with measures A, B, and C, respectively. Then, $$\frac{\sin A}{a} = \frac{\sin B}{b} = \frac{\sin C}{c}.$$

Example: In $\triangle DEF$ find e.

$$\frac{\sin 28°}{12} = \frac{\sin 72°}{e} \quad \text{Use the Law of Sines.}$$

$$e \sin 28° = 12 \sin 72°$$

$$e = \frac{12 \sin 72°}{\sin 28°}$$

Use a calculator to find e.

ENTER: 12 ⊠ 72 [SIN] ÷ 28 [SIN] = 24.30962618

So, $e \approx 24.3$.

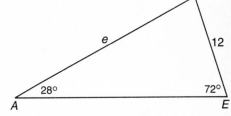

Draw $\triangle RST$ and mark it with the given information. Write an equation that could be used to find each unknown value. Then find the value to the nearest tenth.

1. If $s = 18$, $m\angle R = 32$, and $m\angle S = 47$, find r.

2. If $s = 42$, $t = 29$, and $m\angle S = 63$, find $m\angle T$.

3. If $m\angle R = 40$, $m\angle S = 89$, and $t = 4.8$, find r.

4. If $m\angle R = 46$, $m\angle S = 85$, and $t = 17$, find s.

5. Solve $\triangle ABC$ if $a = 15$, $c = 18$, and $m\angle C = 68$. Round measures to the nearest tenth.

Study Guide

Using the Law of Sines

Trigonometric functions can also be used to solve problems that involve triangles that are not right triangles.

Law of Sines	Let $\triangle ABC$ be any triangle with a, b, and c representing the measures of sides opposite angles with measures A, B, and C, respectively. Then, $$\frac{\sin A}{a} = \frac{\sin B}{b} = \frac{\sin C}{c}.$$

Example: In $\triangle DEF$ find e.

$$\frac{\sin 28°}{12} = \frac{\sin 72°}{e} \qquad \text{Use the Law of Sines.}$$

$$e \sin 28° = 12 \sin 72°$$

$$e = \frac{12 \sin 72°}{\sin 28°}$$

Use a calculator to find e.

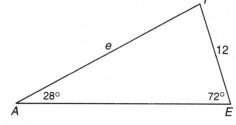

ENTER: 12 ⊠ 72 [SIN] ⊡ 28 [SIN] ⊟ 24.30962618

So, $e \approx 24.3$.

Draw $\triangle RST$ and mark it with the given information. Write an equation that could be used to find each unknown value. Then find the value to the nearest tenth.

1. If $s = 18$, $m\angle R = 32$, and $m\angle S = 47$, find r.

$$\frac{\sin 32°}{r} = \frac{\sin 47°}{18}$$

$$r \approx 13.0$$

2. If $s = 42$, $t = 29$, and $m\angle S = 63$, find $m\angle T$.

$$\frac{\sin 63°}{42} = \frac{\sin T}{29}$$

$$m\angle T \approx 38.0$$

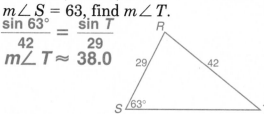

3. If $m\angle R = 40$, $m\angle S = 89$, and $t = 4.8$, find r.

$$\frac{\sin 40°}{r} = \frac{\sin 51°}{4.8}$$

$$r \approx 4.0$$

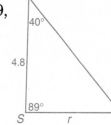

4. If $m\angle R = 46$, $m\angle S = 85$, and $t = 17$, find s.

$$\frac{\sin 85°}{s} = \frac{\sin 49°}{17}$$

$$s \approx 22.4$$

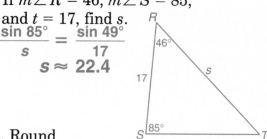

5. Solve $\triangle ABC$ if $a = 15$, $c = 18$, and $m\angle C = 68$. Round measures to the nearest tenth. $m\angle A \approx 50.6$, $m\angle B \approx 61.4$, $b \approx 17.0$

NAME_____ DATE _____

Study Guide

Using the Law of Cosines

The Law of Cosines often allows you to solve a triangle when the Law of Sines cannot be used.

Law of Cosines	Let $\triangle ABC$ be any triangle with a, b, and c representing the measures of sides opposite angles with measures A, B, and C, respectively. Then, the following equations hold true. $a^2 = b^2 + d^2 - 2bc \cos A$ $b^2 = a^2 + c^2 - 2ac \cos B$ $c^2 = a^2 + b^2 - 2ab \cos C$

Example: For $\triangle ABC$, find a if $m\angle A = 28$, $c = 30$, and $b = 17$.

Since the measures of two sides and the included angle are known, this is an example of Case 1 for the Law of Cosines.

$a^2 = b^2 + c^2 - 2bc \cos A$
$a^2 = 17^2 + 30^2 - 2(17)(30) \cos 28$
$a^2 = 289 + 900 - 1020 \cos 28$
$a^2 \approx 288.393$
$a \approx 16.98$

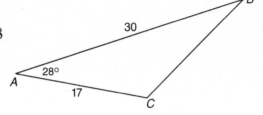

Use a calculator to solve each triangle ABC described below. Round measures to the nearest tenth.

1. $m\angle C = 60$, $a = 12$, $b = 15$

2. $a = 34$, $c = 27$, $m\angle B = 60$

3. $m\angle C = 65$, $a = 8.4$, $b = 9.6$

4. $a = 5$, $b = 9$, $c = 10$

5. Decision Making State whether you would use the Law of Sines or the Law of Cosines to solve $\triangle FGH$.

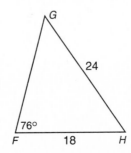

48

Study Guide

Using the Law of Cosines

The Law of Cosines often allows you to solve a triangle when the Law of Sines cannot be used.

Law of Cosines	Let $\triangle ABC$ be any triangle with a, b, and c representing the measures of sides opposite angles with measures A, B, and C, respectively. Then, the following equations hold true. $a^2 = b^2 + d^2 - 2bc \cos A$ $b^2 = a^2 + c^2 - 2ac \cos B$ $c^2 = a^2 + b^2 - 2ab \cos C$

Example: For $\triangle ABC$, find a if $m\angle A = 28$, $c = 30$, and $b = 17$.

Since the measures of two sides and the included angle are known, this is an example of Case 1 for the Law of Cosines.

$a^2 = b^2 + c^2 - 2bc \cos A$
$a^2 = 17^2 + 30^2 - 2(17)(30) \cos 28$
$a^2 = 289 + 900 - 1020 \cos 28$
$a^2 \approx 288.393$
$a \approx 16.98$

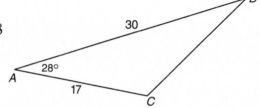

Use a calculator to solve each triangle ABC described below. Round measures to the nearest tenth.

1. $m\angle C = 60$, $a = 12$, $b = 15$
   $c \approx 13.7$, $m\angle A \approx 49.2$, $m\angle B \approx 70.8$

2. $a = 34$, $c = 27$, $m\angle B = 60$
   $b \approx 31.1$, $m\angle A \approx 71.2$,
   $m\angle C \approx 48.8$

3. $m\angle C = 65$, $a = 8.4$, $b = 9.6$
   $c \approx 9.7$, $m\angle A \approx 51.6$, $m\angle B \approx 63.4$

4. $a = 5$, $b = 9$, $c = 10$
   $m\angle C \approx 86.2$, $m\angle A \approx 29.9$,
   $m\angle B \approx 63.9$

5. **Decision Making** State whether you would use the Law of Sines or the Law of Cosines to solve $\triangle FGH$. **Law of Sines**

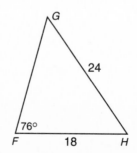

Geometry

Study Guide

Exploring Circles

A **circle** is the set of all points in a plane that are a given distance from a given point in the plane called the **center**. Various parts of a circle are labeled in the figure at the right.

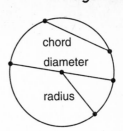

The distance around a circle is called the **circumference**.

Circumference of a Circle	If a circle has a circumference of C units and a radius of r units, then $C = 2\pi r$.

Example: Find the circumference of the circle shown at the right.

$$C = 2\pi r$$
$$C = 2\pi(13)$$
$$C = 26\pi$$
$$C \approx 81.7$$

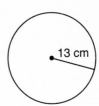

The circumference is about 81.7 cm.

Refer to ⊙*S for Exercises 1–6.*

1. Name the center of ⊙S.

2. Name three radii of ⊙S.

3. Name a diameter.

4. Name a chord.

5. If $RT = 8.2$, find SM.

6. Is $\overline{SR} \cong \overline{SM}$? Explain.

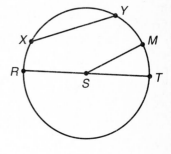

In Exercises 7–10, the radius, diameter, or circumference of a circle is given. Find the other measures to the nearest tenth.

7. $r = 7$, $d = \underline{\ ?\ }$, $C = \underline{\ ?\ }$ 8. $d = 32.4$, $r = \underline{\ ?\ }$, $C = \underline{\ ?\ }$

9. $C = 116.5$, $d = \underline{\ ?\ }$, $r = \underline{\ ?\ }$ 10. $r = 12$, $d = \underline{\ ?\ }$, $C = \underline{\ ?\ }$

9-1

Study Guide

Exploring Circles

A **circle** is the set of all points in a plane that are a given distance from a given point in the plane called the **center**. Various parts of a circle are labeled in the figure at the right.

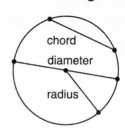

The distance around a circle is called the **circumference**.

Circumference of a Circle	If a circle has a circumference of C units and a radius of r units, then $C = 2\pi r$.

Example: Find the circumference of the circle shown at the right.

$$C = 2\pi r$$
$$C = 2\pi(13)$$
$$C = 26\pi$$
$$C \approx 81.7$$

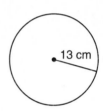

The circumference is about 81.7 cm.

Refer to ⊙S for Exercises 1–6.

1. Name the center of ⊙S. **S**

2. Name three radii of ⊙S. **$\overline{SR}$, $\overline{SM}$, $\overline{ST}$**

3. Name a diameter. **$\overline{RT}$**

4. Name a chord. **$\overline{XY}$, or $\overline{RT}$**

5. If $RT = 8.2$, find SM. **4.1**

6. Is $\overline{SR} \cong \overline{SM}$? Explain. **Yes; they are both radii of ⊙S.**

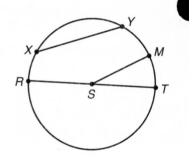

In Exercises 7–10, the radius, diameter, or circumference of a circle is given. Find the other measures to the nearest tenth.

7. $r = 7$, $d = \underline{?}$, $C = \underline{?}$ **14.0; 44.0**

8. $d = 32.4$, $r = \underline{?}$, $C = \underline{?}$ **16.2; 101.8**

9. $C = 116.5$, $d = \underline{?}$, $r = \underline{?}$ **37.1; 18.6**

10. $r = 12$, $d = \underline{?}$, $C = \underline{?}$ **24; 75.4**

NAME _____ DATE _____

Student Edition
Pages 452–458

Study Guide

Angles and Arcs

An angle whose vertex is at the center of a circle is called a **central angle**. A central angle separates a circle into two arcs called a **major arc** and a **minor arc**. In the circle at the right, $\angle CEF$ is a central angle. Points C and F and all points of the circle interior to $\angle CEF$ form a minor arc called arc CF. This is written $\overset{\frown}{CF}$. Points C and F and all points of the circle exterior to $\angle CEF$ form a major arc called $\overset{\frown}{CGF}$.

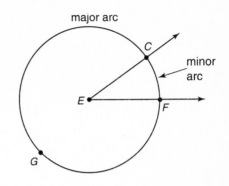

You can use central angles to find both the degree measure and the length of an arc. The arcs determined by a diameter are called semicircles and have measures of 180.

Examples: In $\odot R$, $m\angle ARB = 42$, $RB = 12$, and $\overline{AC}$ is a diameter.

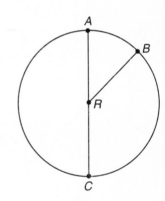

1 Find $m\overset{\frown}{AB}$ and $m\overset{\frown}{ACB}$.
Since $\angle ARB$ is a central angle and $m\angle ARB = 42$, then $m\overset{\frown}{AB} = 42$.
$m\overset{\frown}{ACB} = 360 - m\overset{\frown}{AB} = 360 - 42$ or 318

2 Find the length of $\overset{\frown}{AB}$.
First, find what part of the circle is represented by $\angle ARB$.

$$\frac{42}{360} = \frac{7}{60}$$

So, the length of $\overset{\frown}{AB}$ is $\frac{7}{60}$ of the circumference of $\odot R$.

length of $\overset{\frown}{AB} = \frac{7}{60}(2\pi r)$

$\qquad = \frac{7}{60}(2\pi)(12)$ or about 8.8 units

Refer to $\odot P$ for Exercises 1–8. If $\overline{SN}$ and $\overline{MT}$ are diameters with $m\angle SPT = 51$ and $m\angle NPR = 29$, determine whether each arc is a minor arc, a major arc, or a semicircle. Then find the degree measure of each arc.

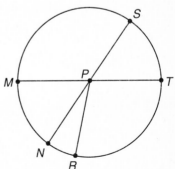

1. $m\overset{\frown}{NR}$

2. $m\overset{\frown}{ST}$

3. $m\overset{\frown}{TSR}$

4. $m\overset{\frown}{MST}$

If $MT = 15$, find the length of each arc. Round to the nearest tenth.

5. $\overset{\frown}{NR}$

6. $\overset{\frown}{ST}$

7. $\overset{\frown}{TSR}$

8. $\overset{\frown}{MST}$

Geometry

Study Guide

Angles and Arcs

An angle whose vertex is at the center of a circle is called a **central angle**. A central angle separates a circle into two arcs called a **major arc** and a **minor arc**. In the circle at the right, $\angle CEF$ is a central angle. Points C and F and all points of the circle interior to $\angle CEF$ form a minor arc called arc CF. This is written $\widehat{CF}$. Points C and F and all points of the circle exterior to $\angle CEF$ form a major arc called $\widehat{CGF}$.

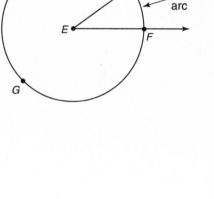

You can use central angles to find both the degree measure and the length of an arc. The arcs determined by a diameter are called semicircles and have measures of 180.

Examples: In $\odot R$, $m\angle ARB = 42$, $RB = 12$, and $\overline{AC}$ is a diameter.

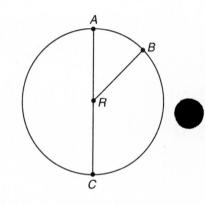

1 Find $m\widehat{AB}$ and $m\widehat{ACB}$.
Since $\angle ARB$ is a central angle and $m\angle ARB = 42$, then $m\widehat{AB} = 42$.
$m\widehat{ACB} = 360 - m\widehat{AB} = 360 - 42$ or 318

2 Find the length of $\widehat{AB}$.
First, find what part of the circle is represented by $\angle ARB$.

$$\frac{42}{360} = \frac{7}{60}$$

So, the length of $\widehat{AB}$ is $\frac{7}{60}$ of the circumference of $\odot R$.

$$\text{length of } \widehat{AB} = \frac{7}{60}(2\pi r)$$
$$= \frac{7}{60}(2\pi)(12) \text{ or about } 8.8 \text{ units}$$

Refer to $\odot P$ for Exercises 1–8. If $\overline{SN}$ and $\overline{MT}$ are diameters with $m\angle SPT = 51$ and $m\angle NPR = 29$, determine whether each arc is a minor arc, a major arc, or a semicircle. Then find the degree measure of each arc.

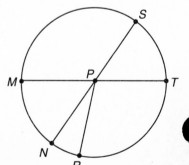

1. $m\widehat{NR}$ minor; 29

2. $m\widehat{ST}$ minor; 51

3. $m\widehat{TSR}$ major; 260

4. $m\widehat{MST}$ semicircle; 180

If $MT = 15$, find the length of each arc. Round to the nearest tenth.

5. $\widehat{NR}$ 3.8

6. $\widehat{ST}$ 6.7

7. $\widehat{TSR}$ 34.0

8. $\widehat{MST}$ 23.6

Study Guide

Arcs and Chords

The following theorems state relationships between arcs, chords, and diameters.

- In a circle or in congruent circles, two minor arcs are congruent if and only if their corresponding chords are congruent.

- In a circle, if a diameter is perpendicular to a chord, then it bisects the chord and its arc.

- In a circle or in congruent circles, two chords are congruent if and only if they are equidistant from the center.

Example: In the circle, O is the center, $OD = 15$, and $CD = 24$. Find x.

$$ED = \frac{1}{2} CD$$
$$= \frac{1}{2} (24)$$
$$= 12$$

$$(OE)^2 + (ED)^2 = (OD)^2$$
$$x^2 + 12^2 = 15^2$$
$$x^2 + 144 = 225$$
$$x^2 = 81$$
$$x = 9$$

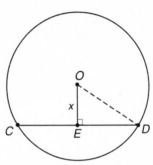

In each circle, O is the center. Find each measure.

1. $m\overarc{NP}$

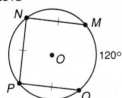

2. KM

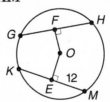

3. XY

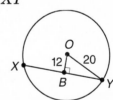

4. Suppose a chord is 20 inches long and is 24 inches from the center of the circle. Find the length of the radius.

5. Suppose a chord of a circle is 5 inches from the center and is 24 inches long. Find the length of the radius.

6. Suppose the diameter of a circle is 30 centimeters long and a chord is 24 centimeters long. Find the distance between the chord and the center of the circle.

9–3

Study Guide

Arcs and Chords

The following theorems state relationships between arcs, chords, and diameters.

- In a circle or in congruent circles, two minor arcs are congruent if and only if their corresponding chords are congruent.

- In a circle, if a diameter is perpendicular to a chord, then it bisects the chord and its arc.

- In a circle or in congruent circles, two chords are congruent if and only if they are equidistant from the center.

Example: In the circle, O is the center, $OD = 15$, and $CD = 24$. Find x.

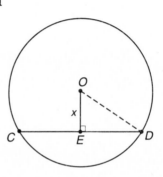

$$ED = \frac{1}{2}\,CD$$
$$= \frac{1}{2}\,(24)$$
$$= 12$$

$$(OE)^2 + (ED)^2 = (OD)^2$$
$$x^2 + 12^2 = 15^2$$
$$x^2 + 144 = 225$$
$$x^2 = 81$$
$$x = 9$$

In each circle, O is the center. Find each measure.

1. $m\widehat{NP}$

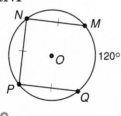

80

2. KM

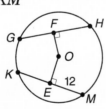

24

3. XY

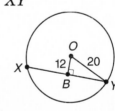

32

4. Suppose a chord is 20 inches long and is 24 inches from the center of the circle. Find the length of the radius. **26 in.**

5. Suppose a chord of a circle is 5 inches from the center and is 24 inches long. Find the length of the radius. **13 in.**

6. Suppose the diameter of a circle is 30 centimeters long and a chord is 24 centimeters long. Find the distance between the chord and the center of the circle. **9 cm**

T51

9-4

Study Guide

Inscribed Angles

An **inscribed angle** of a circle is an angle whose vertex is on the circle and whose sides contain chords of the circle. We say that $\angle DEF$ intercepts $\overset{\frown}{DF}$. The following theorems involve inscribed angles.

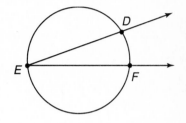

- If an angle is inscribed in a circle, then the measure of the angle equals one-half the measure of its intercepted arc.

- If two inscribed angles of a circle or congruent circles intercept congruent arcs or the same arc, then the angles are congruent.

- If an inscribed angle of a circle intercepts a semicircle, then the angle is a right angle.

- If a quadrilateral is inscribed in a circle, then its opposite angles are supplementary.

Example: In the circle above, find $m\angle DEF$ if $m\overset{\frown}{DF} = 28$.
Since $\angle DEF$ is an inscribed angle,
$m\angle DEF = \frac{1}{2} m\overset{\frown}{DF} = \frac{1}{2}(28)$ or 14.

In ⊙P, $\overset{\frown}{RS} \parallel \overset{\frown}{TV}$.

1. Name the intercepted arc for $\angle RTS$.

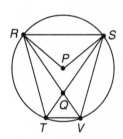

2. Name an inscribed angle.

3. Name a central angle.

In ⊙P, $m\overset{\frown}{SV} = 86$ and $m\angle RPS = 110$. Find each measure.

4. $m\angle PRS$ **5.** $m\overset{\frown}{RT}$ **6.** $m\angle RVT$ **7.** $m\angle SVT$

8. $m\angle TQV$ **9.** $m\angle RQT$ **10.** $m\angle QRT$ **11.** $m\overset{\frown}{RS}$

9–4

Study Guide

Inscribed Angles

An **inscribed angle** of a circle is an angle whose vertex is
on the circle and whose sides contain chords of the circle.
We say that $\angle DEF$ intercepts $\overset{\frown}{DF}$. The following theorems
involve inscribed angles.

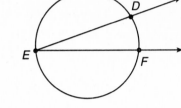

- If an angle is inscribed in a circle, then the measure of
  the angle equals one-half the measure of its intercepted
  arc.

- If two inscribed angles of a circle or congruent circles
  intercept congruent arcs or the same arc, then the
  angles are congruent.

- If an inscribed angle of a circle intercepts a semicircle,
  then the angle is a right angle.

- If a quadrilateral is inscribed in a circle, then its
  opposite angles are supplementary.

Example: In the circle above, find $m\angle DEF$ if $m\overset{\frown}{DF} = 28$.
Since $\angle DEF$ is an inscribed angle,
$m\angle DEF = \frac{1}{2} m\overset{\frown}{DF} = \frac{1}{2}(28)$ or 14.

In ⊙P, 

1. Name the intercepted arc for $\angle RTS$. $\overset{\frown}{RS}$

2. Name an inscribed angle.

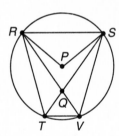

3. Name a central angle. $\angle RPS$

In ⊙P, $m\overset{\frown}{SV} = 86$ and $m\angle RPS = 110$. Find each measure.

4. $m\angle PRS$	5. $m\overset{\frown}{RT}$	6. $m\angle RVT$	7. $m\angle SVT$
35	86	43	98

8. $m\angle TQV$	9. $m\angle RQT$	10. $m\angle QRT$	11. $m\overset{\frown}{RS}$
94	86	39	110

Study Guide

Tangents

Remember that a tangent is a line in the plane of a circle that intersects the circle in exactly one point. Three important theorems involving tangents are the following.

- If a line is a tangent to a circle, then it is perpendicular to the radius drawn to the point of tangency.

- In a plane, if a line is perpendicular to a radius of a circle at the endpoint on the circle, then the line is a tangent of the circle.

- If two segments from the same exterior point are tangent to a circle, then they are congruent.

Example: Find the value of x if $\overline{AB}$ is tangent to $\odot C$.

Tangent $\overline{AB}$ is perpendicular to radius $\overline{BC}$. Also, $AC = AD + BC = 17$.

$$(AB)^2 + (BC)^2 = (AC)^2$$
$$x^2 + 8^2 = 17^2$$
$$x^2 + 64 = 289$$
$$x^2 = 225$$
$$x = 15$$

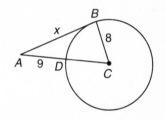

For each $\odot C$, find the value of x. Assume that segments that appear to be tangent are tangent.

1.

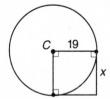

2.

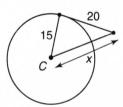

3.

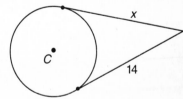

4.

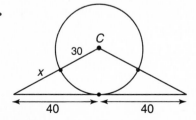

5.

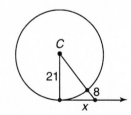

6.

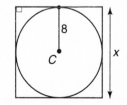

Tangents

Remember that a tangent is a line in the plane of a circle that intersects the circle in exactly one point. Three important theorems involving tangents are the following.

- If a line is a tangent to a circle, then it is perpendicular to the radius drawn to the point of tangency.

- In a plane, if a line is perpendicular to a radius of a circle at the endpoint on the circle, then the line is a tangent of the circle.

- If two segments from the same exterior point are tangent to a circle, then they are congruent.

Example: Find the value of x if $\overline{AB}$ is tangent to $\odot C$.

Tangent $\overline{AB}$ is perpendicular to radius $\overline{BC}$. Also, $AC = AD + BC = 17$.

$$(AB)^2 + (BC)^2 = (AC)^2$$
$$x^2 + 8^2 = 17^2$$
$$x^2 + 64 = 289$$
$$x^2 = 225$$
$$x = 15$$

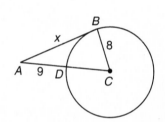

For each $\odot C$, find the value of x. Assume that segments that appear to be tangent are tangent.

1.

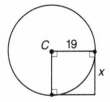

19

2.

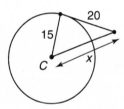

25

3.

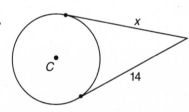

14

4.

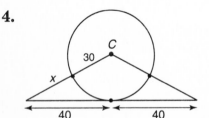

20

5.

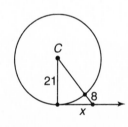

20

6.

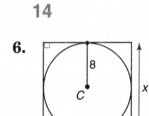

16

Secants, Tangents, and Angle Measures

A line that intersects a circle in exactly two points is called a **secant** of the circle. You can find the measures of angles formed by secants and tangents by using the following theorems.

- If a secant and a tangent intersect at the point of tangency, then the measure of each angle formed is one-half the measure of its intercepted arc.

- If two secants intersect in the interior of a circle, then the measure of an angle formed is one-half the sum of the measures of the arcs intercepted by the angle and its vertical angle.

- If two secants, a secant and a tangent, or two tangents intersect in the exterior of a circle, then the measure of the angle formed is one-half the positive difference of the measures of the intercepted arcs.

Example: Find the measure of $\angle MPN$.

You can use the last theorem above.

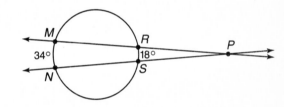

$$m\angle MPN = \frac{1}{2} m(\overset{\frown}{MN} - \overset{\frown}{RS})$$
$$= \frac{1}{2}(34 - 18)$$
$$= \frac{1}{2}(16) \text{ or } 8$$

Find the measure of each numbered angle.

1.

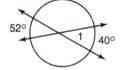

2.

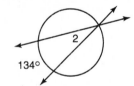

3.

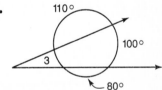

Given ⊙T, find the value of x.

4.

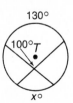

5.

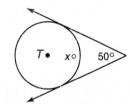

6.

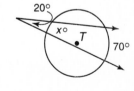

Geometry

Study Guide

Secants, Tangents, and Angle Measures

A line that intersects a circle in exactly two points is called a **secant** of the circle. You can find the measures of angles formed by secants and tangents by using the following theorems.

- If a secant and a tangent intersect at the point of tangency, then the measure of each angle formed is one-half the measure of its intercepted arc.

- If two secants intersect in the interior of a circle, then the measure of an angle formed is one-half the sum of the measures of the arcs intercepted by the angle and its vertical angle.

- If two secants, a secant and a tangent, or two tangents intersect in the exterior of a circle, then the measure of the angle formed is one-half the positive difference of the measures of the intercepted arcs.

Example: Find the measure of $\angle MPN$.

You can use the last theorem above.

$$m\angle MPN = \tfrac{1}{2}\, m(\widehat{MN} - \widehat{RS})$$
$$= \tfrac{1}{2}(34 - 18)$$
$$= \tfrac{1}{2}(16) \text{ or } 8$$

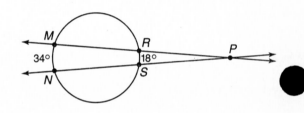

Find the measure of each numbered angle.

1.

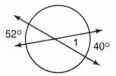

46

2.

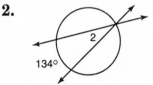

67

3.

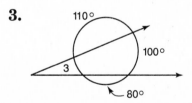

15

Given ⊙T, find the value of x.

4.

70

5.

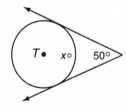

130

6.

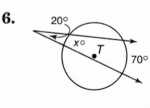

30

Study Guide

Special Segments in a Circle

The following theorems can be used to find the measure of special segments in a circle.

- If two chords intersect in a circle, then the products of the measures of the segments of the chords are equal.

- If two segments are drawn to a circle from an exterior point, then the product of the measures of one secant segment and its external secant segment is equal to the product of the measures of the other secant segment and its external secant segment.

- If a tangent segment and a secant segment are drawn to a circle from an exterior point, then the square of the measure of the tangent segment is equal to the product of the measures of the secant segment and its external secant segment.

Example: Find the value of x to the nearest tenth.

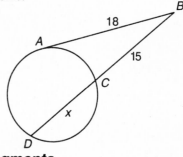

$$(AB)^2 = BC \cdot BD \qquad \text{Theorem 9–16}$$
$$(18)^2 = 15 \cdot (15 + x)$$
$$324 = 225 + 15x$$
$$99 = 15x$$
$$6.6 = x$$

Find the value of x to the nearest tenth. Assume segments that appear tangent to be tangent.

1.

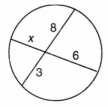

2.

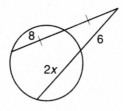

3.

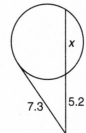

4.

5.

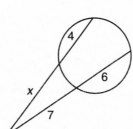

6.

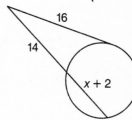

7.

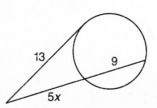

8.

9.

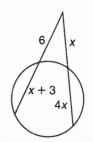

Study Guide

Special Segments in a Circle

The following theorems can be used to find the measure of
special segments in a circle.

- If two chords intersect in a circle, then the products of the
  measures of the segments of the chords are equal.

- If two segments are drawn to a circle from an exterior point,
  then the product of the measures of one secant segment and
  its external secant segment is equal to the product of the
  measures of the other secant segment and its external secant
  segment.

- If a tangent segment and a secant segment are drawn to a
  circle from an exterior point, then the square of the measure
  of the tangent segment is equal to the product of the measures
  of the secant segment and its external secant segment.

Example: Find the value of x to the nearest tenth.

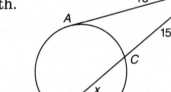

$$(AB)^2 = BC \cdot BD \qquad \textbf{Theorem 9-16}$$
$$(18)^2 = 15 \cdot (15 + x)$$
$$324 = 225 + 15x$$
$$99 = 15x$$
$$6.6 = x$$

**Find the value of x to the nearest tenth. Assume segments
that appear tangent to be tangent.**

1.

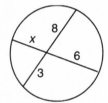

4

2.

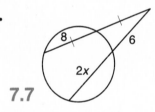

7.7

3.

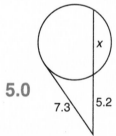

5.0

4.

4

5.

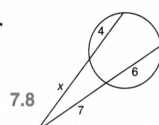

7.8

6.

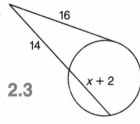

2.3

7.

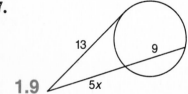

1.9

8.

1.7

9.

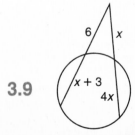

3.9

Integration: Algebra
Equations of Circles

The **standard equation for a circle** is derived from using the distance formula given the coordinates of the center of the circle and the measure of its radius. An equation for a circle with center (h, k) and a radius of r units is $(x - h)^2 + (y - k)^2 = r^2$.

Example: Graph the circle whose equation is $(x + 3)^2 + (y - 1)^2 = 16$.

$$(x - h)^2 + (y - k)^2 = r^2 \quad \text{standard equation}$$
$$(x - (-3))^2 + (y - 1)^2 = (\sqrt{16})^2 \quad \text{rewrite equation in standard form}$$

Therefore, $h = -3$, $k = 1$, and $r = \sqrt{16} = 4$.
The center is at $(-3, 1)$ and the radius is 4 units.

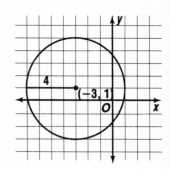

Determine the coordinates of the center and the measure of the radius for each circle whose equation is given.

1. $(x - 7.2)^2 + (y + 3.4)^2 = 14.44$

2. $\left(x + \dfrac{1}{2}\right)^2 + (y - 2)^2 = \dfrac{16}{25}$

3. $(x - 6)^2 + (y - 3)^2 - 25 = 0$

Graph each circle whose equation is given. Label the center and measure of the radius on each graph.

4. $(x - 2.5)^2 + (y + 1)^2 = 12.25$

5. $(x + 3)^2 + (y - 4)^2 - 2.25 = 0$

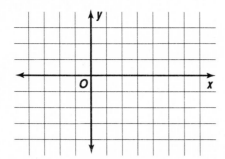

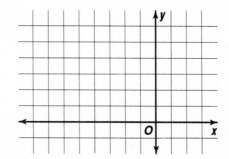

6. $\left(x - \dfrac{1}{2}\right)^2 + \left(y - \dfrac{3}{4}\right)^2 = 1$

7. $x^2 + (y - 2)^2 = 9$

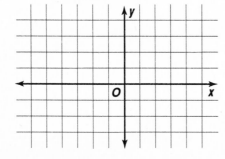

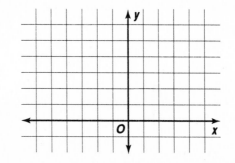

NAME_____ DATE _____

Study Guide

Integration: Algebra
Equations of Circles

The **standard equation for a circle** is derived from using the distance formula given the coordinates of the center of the circle and the measure of its radius. An equation for a circle with center (h, k) and a radius of r units is $(x - h)^2 + (y - k)^2 = r^2$.

Example: Graph the circle whose equation is $(x + 3)^2 + (y - 1)^2 = 16$.

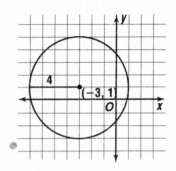

$$(x - h)^2 + (y - k)^2 = r^2 \qquad \text{standard equation}$$
$$(x - (-3))^2 + (y - 1)^2 = (\sqrt{16})^2 \qquad \text{rewrite equation in standard form}$$

Therefore, $h = -3$, $k = 1$, and $r = \sqrt{16} = 4$.
The center is at $(-3, 1)$ and the radius is 4 units.

Determine the coordinates of the center and the measure of the radius for each circle whose equation is given.

1. $(x - 7.2)^2 + (y + 3.4)^2 = 14.44$
(7.2, -3.4), r = 3.8

2. $\left(x + \dfrac{1}{2}\right)^2 + (y - 2)^2 = \dfrac{16}{25}$
$\left(-\dfrac{1}{2}, 2\right), r = \dfrac{4}{5}$

3. $(x - 6)^2 + (y - 3)^2 - 25 = 0$ **(6, 3), r = 5**

Graph each circle whose equation is given. Label the center and measure of the radius on each graph.

4. $(x - 2.5)^2 + (y + 1)^2 = 12.25$

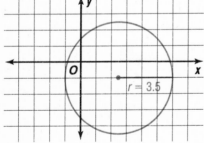

5. $(x + 3)^2 + (y - 4)^2 - 2.25 = 0$

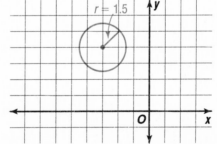

6. $\left(x - \dfrac{1}{2}\right)^2 + \left(y - \dfrac{3}{4}\right)^2 = 1$

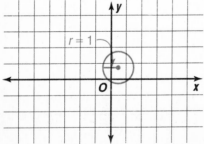

7. $x^2 + (y - 2)^2 = 9$

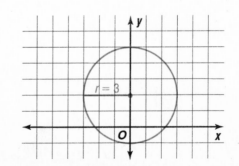

NAME_____ DATE _____

Study Guide

Polygons

A **polygon** is a plane figure formed by a finite number of segments such that (1) sides that have a common endpoint are noncollinear and (2) each side intersects exactly two other sides, but only at their endpoints. A **convex polygon** is a polygon such that no line containing a side of the polygon contains a point in the interior of the polygon. Convex polygons with all sides congruent and all angles congruent are called **regular**.

The following two theorems involve the interior and exterior angles of a convex polygon.

Interior Angle Sum Theorem	If a convex polygon has n sides and S is the sum of the measures of its interior angles, then $S = 180(n - 2)$.
Exterior Angle Sum Theorem	If a polygon is convex, then the sum of the measures of the exterior angles, one at each vertex, is 360.

Example: Find the sum of the measures of the interior angles of a convex polygon with 13 sides.

$S = 180(n - 2)$ **Interior Angle Sum Theorem**
$S = 180(13 - 2)$
$S = 180(11)$
$S = 1980$

Find the sum of the measures of the interior angles of each convex polygon.

1. 10-gon   2. 16-gon   3. 30-gon

The measure of an exterior angle of a regular polygon is given. Find the number of sides of the polygon.

4. 30   5. 20   6. 5

The number of sides of a regular polygon is given. Find the measures of an interior angle and an exterior angle for each polygon.

7. 18   8. 36   9. 25

10. The measure of the interior angle of a regular polygon is 157.5. Find the number of sides of the polygon.

NAME_____ DATE _____

Study Guide

Polygons

A **polygon** is a plane figure formed by a finite number of segments such that (1) sides that have a common endpoint are noncollinear and (2) each side intersects exactly two other sides, but only at their endpoints. A **convex polygon** is a polygon such that no line containing a side of the polygon contains a point in the interior of the polygon. Convex polygons with all sides congruent and all angles congruent are called **regular**.

The following two theorems involve the interior and exterior angles of a convex polygon.

Interior Angle Sum Theorem	If a convex polygon has n sides and S is the sum of the measures of its interior angles, then $S = 180(n - 2)$.
Exterior Angle Sum Theorem	If a polygon is convex, then the sum of the measures of the exterior angles, one at each vertex, is 360.

Example: Find the sum of the measures of the interior angles of a convex polygon with 13 sides.

$S = 180(n - 2)$ **Interior Angle Sum Theorem**
$S = 180(13 - 2)$
$S = 180(11)$
$S = 1980$

Find the sum of the measures of the interior angles of each convex polygon.

1. 10-gon **1440**

2. 16-gon **2520**

3. 30-gon **5040**

The measure of an exterior angle of a regular polygon is given. Find the number of sides of the polygon.

4. 30 **12**

5. 20 **18**

6. 5 **72**

The number of sides of a regular polygon is given. Find the measures of an interior angle and an exterior angle for each polygon.

7. 18 **160; 20**

8. 36 **170; 10**

9. 25 **165.6; 14.4**

10. The measure of the interior angle of a regular polygon is 157.5. Find the number of sides of the polygon. **16**

NAME_____ DATE _____

Study Guide

Student Edition
Pages 523–527

Tessellations

Tessellations are patterns that cover a plane with repeating polygons so that there are no overlapping or empty spaces. A **regular tessellation** uses only one type of regular polygon. **Uniform tessellations** contain the same combination of shapes and angles at each vertex. **Semi-regular tessellations** are uniform tessellations that contain two or more regular polygons.

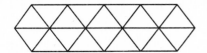

regular, uniform

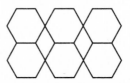

semi-regular

In a tessellation, the sum of the measures of the angles of the polygons surrounding a point (at a vertex) is 360. If a regular polygon has an interior angle with a measure that is a factor of 360, then the polygon will tessellate.

Example: Determine if a regular 16-gon will tessellate

$$\frac{(180 - n)}{n}$$ **Use this formula to find the measure of each interior angle.**

$$\frac{(180 - 16)}{16} = 10.25 \qquad n = 16$$

Since 10.25 is not a factor of 360, the 16-gon will not tessellate.

Determine whether each figure tessellates in a plane. If so, draw a sample figure.

1. scalene right triangle   **2.** regular nonagon   **3.** isosceles trapezoid

Determine if each pattern will tessellate.

4. square and isosceles triangle

5. rhombus, triangle, and octagon

6. square and isosceles trapezoid

Geometry

Study Guide

Tessellations

Tessellations are patterns that cover a plane with repeating polygons so that there are no overlapping or empty spaces. A **regular tessellation** uses only one type of regular polygon. **Uniform tessellations** contain the same combination of shapes and angles at each vertex. **Semi-regular tessellations** are uniform tessellations that contain two or more regular polygons.

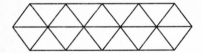

regular, uniform

semi-regular

In a tessellation, the sum of the measures of the angles of the polygons surrounding a point (at a vertex) is 360. If a regular polygon has an interior angle with a measure that is a factor of 360, then the polygon will tessellate.

Example: Determine if a regular 16-gon will tessellate

$$\frac{(180 - n)}{n}$$ Use this formula to find the measure of each interior angle.

$$\frac{(180 - 16)}{16} = 10.25 \qquad n = 16$$

Since 10.25 is not a factor of 360, the 16-gon will not tessellate.

Determine whether each figure tessellates in a plane. If so, draw a sample figure.

1. scalene right triangle
   yes

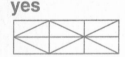

2. regular nonagon
   no

3. isosceles trapezoid
   yes

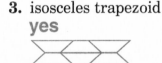

Determine if each pattern will tessellate.

4. square and isosceles triangle **yes**

5. rhombus, triangle, and octagon **no**

6. square and isosceles trapezoid **yes**

Study Guide

Area of Parallelograms

The area of a parallelogram is the same as the area of a rectangle that has the same base and height.

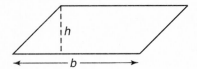 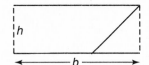

> If a parallelogram has an area of *A* square units, a base of *b* units, and a height of *h* units, then $A = bh$.

The area of a region is the sum of the areas of all of its nonoverlapping parts.

Example: Find the area of the parallelogram.

$A = bh$
$A = 3.6(2.4)$
$A = 8.64$

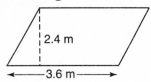

The area is 8.64 m².

Find the area of each figure.

1.
   19 m
   15 m

2.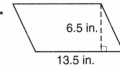
   6.5 in.
   13.5 in.

3.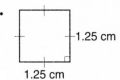
   1.25 cm
   1.25 cm

Find the area of each shaded region. Assume that angles that appear to be right are right angles.

4.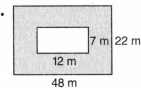
   7 m | 22 m
   12 m
   48 m

5.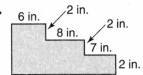
   6 in. 2 in.
   8 in. 2 in.
   7 in.
   2 in.

6.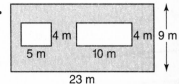
   4 m | 4 m | 9 m
   5 m | 10 m
   23 m

7. The area of a parallelogram is 24.96 cm². The base is 6.4 cm. If the measures of the base and height are each doubled, find the area of the resulting parallelogram.

8. A rectangle is 6 meters longer than it is wide. The area of the rectangle is 315 square meters. Find the length.

NAME_____ DATE _____

Study Guide

Area of Parallelograms

The area of a parallelogram is the same as the area of a rectangle that has the same base and height.

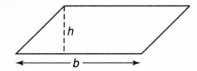 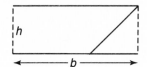

> If a parallelogram has an area of *A* square units, a base of *b* units, and a height of *h* units, then $A = bh$.

The area of a region is the sum of the areas of all of its nonoverlapping parts.

Example: Find the area of the parallelogram.

$A = bh$
$A = 3.6(2.4)$
$A = 8.64$

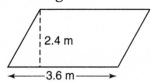

The area is 8.64 m².

Find the area of each figure.

1.

19 m
15 m

285 m²

2.

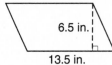

6.5 in.
13.5 in.

87.75 in²

3.

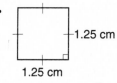

1.25 cm
1.25 cm

1.5625 cm²

Find the area of each shaded region. Assume that angles that appear to be right are right angles.

4.

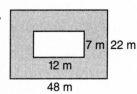

7 m   22 m
12 m
48 m

972 m²

5.

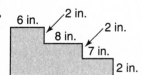

6 in.   2 in.
8 in.   2 in.
7 in.
2 in.

82 in²

6.

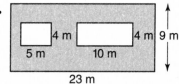

4 m   4 m   9 m
5 m   10 m
23 m

147 m²

7. The area of a parallelogram is 24.96 cm². The base is 6.4 cm. If the measures of the base and height are each doubled, find the area of the resulting parallelogram. **99.84 cm²**

8. A rectangle is 6 meters longer than it is wide. The area of the rectangle is 315 square meters. Find the length. **21 m**

10-4

Study Guide

Area of Triangles, Rhombi, and Trapezoids

Formulas for the areas of triangles, trapezoids, and rhombi can be obtained from the formula for the area of a parallelogram.

triangle
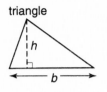

$$A = \frac{1}{2}bh$$

trapezoid
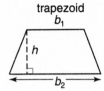

$$A = \frac{1}{2}h(b_1 + b_2)$$

rhombus
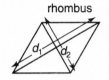

$$A = \frac{1}{2}d_1 d_2$$

Example: Find the area of the trapezoid.

$$A = \frac{1}{2}h(b_1 + b_2)$$

$$A = \frac{1}{2}(10)(12 + 19)$$

$$A = 155$$

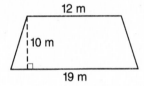

The area is 155 square meters

Find the area of each figure.

1.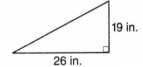

2.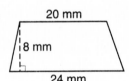

3.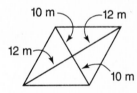

4.

5.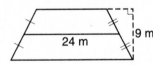

6.

7. The area of a triangle is 150 square inches. If the height is 20 inches, find the length of the base.

8. A rhombus has a perimeter of 100 meters and a diagonal 30 meters long. Find the area of the rhombus.

Geometry

Study Guide

Area of Triangles, Rhombi, and Trapezoids

Formulas for the areas of triangles, trapezoids, and rhombi can be obtained from the formula for the area of a parallelogram.

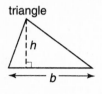

triangle

$$A = \frac{1}{2}bh$$

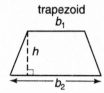

trapezoid

$$A = \frac{1}{2}h(b_1 + b_2)$$

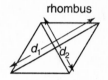

rhombus

$$A = \frac{1}{2}d_1d_2$$

Example: Find the area of the trapezoid.

$$A = \frac{1}{2}h(b_1 + b_2)$$
$$A = \frac{1}{2}(10)(12 + 19)$$
$$A = 155$$

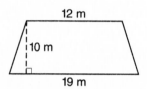

The area is 155 square meters

Find the area of each figure.

1.

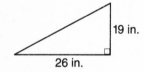

19 in.

26 in.

247 in²

2.

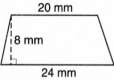

20 mm

8 mm

24 mm

176 mm²

3.

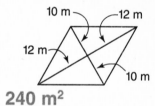

10 m   12 m

12 m

10 m

240 m²

4.

10 m

12 m

96 m²

5.

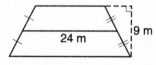

24 m

9 m

216 m²

6.

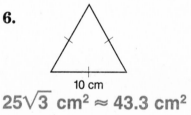

10 cm

25√3 cm² ≈ 43.3 cm²

7. The area of a triangle is 150 square inches. If the height is 20 inches, find the length of the base. **15 in.**

8. A rhombus has a perimeter of 100 meters and a diagonal 30 meters long. Find the area of the rhombus. **600 m²**

10–5

Study Guide

Area of Regular Polygons and Circles

In a regular polygon, a segment drawn from the center of the polygon perpendicular to a side of the polygon is called an **apothem**. In the figure at the right, $\overline{PS}$ is an apothem.

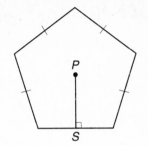

Area of a Regular Polygon	If a regular polygon has an area of A square units, a perimeter of P units, and an apothem of a units, then $A = \frac{1}{2}Pa$.
Area of a Circle	If a circle has an area of A square units and a radius of r units, then $A = \pi r^2$.

Example: Find the area of a regular pentagon with an apothem of 2.8 cm and a perimeter of 20.34 cm.

$$A = \frac{1}{2}Pa \qquad \text{area of a regular polygon}$$
$$A = \frac{1}{2}(20.34)(2.8)$$
$$A = 28.476$$

The area is 28.476 square centimeters.

Find the apothem, area, and perimeter of each regular polygon. Round your answers to the nearest tenth.

1.

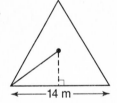

←——14 m——→

2.

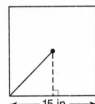

←—— 15 in.——→

3.

10 m

Find the area of each regular polygon described. Round your answers to the nearest tenth.

4. a hexagon with an apothem of $5\sqrt{3}$ cm

5. a pentagon with a perimeter of 54.49 m and an apothem of 7.5 m

Find the area of each shaded region. Assume that all polygons are regular. Round your answers to the nearest tenth.

6.

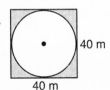

40 m

40 m

7.

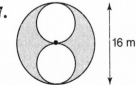

16 m

Study Guide

Area of Regular Polygons and Circles

In a regular polygon, a segment drawn from the center of the polygon perpendicular to a side of the polygon is called an **apothem**. In the figure at the right, $\overline{PS}$ is an apothem.

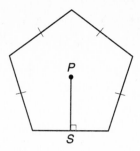

Area of a Regular Polygon	If a regular polygon has an area of A square units, a perimeter of P units, and an apothem of a units, then $A = \frac{1}{2}Pa$.
Area of a Circle	If a circle has an area of A square units and a radius of r units, then $A = \pi r^2$.

Example: Find the area of a regular pentagon with an apothem of 2.8 cm and a perimeter of 20.34 cm.

$A = \frac{1}{2}Pa$ **area of a regular polygon**

$A = \frac{1}{2}(20.34)(2.8)$

$A = 28.476$

The area is 28.476 square centimeters.

Find the apothem, area, and perimeter of each regular polygon. Round your answers to the nearest tenth.

1.

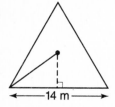

14 m

42 m, 120,
4.0, 84 m²

2.

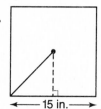

15 in.

60 in., 90,
7.5 in., 225 in²

3.

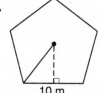

10 m

50 m, 72, 6.9 m,
172.5 m²

Find the area of each regular polygon described. Round your answers to the nearest tenth.

4. a hexagon with an apothem of $5\sqrt{3}$ cm **259.8 cm²**

5. a pentagon with a perimeter of 54.49 m and an apothem of 7.5 m **204.3 m²**

Find the area of each shaded region. Assume that all polygons are regular. Round your answers to the nearest tenth.

6.

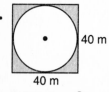

40 m

40 m

343.4 m²

7.

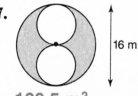

16 m

100.5 m²

Study Guide

Integration: Probability
Geometric Probability

Geometric probability involves using length and area to find the probability of an event.

- If a point on $\overline{AB}$ is chosen at random and C is between A and B, then the probability that the point is on AC is $\frac{\text{length of } \overline{AC}}{\text{length of } \overline{AB}}$.

- If a point in region A is chosen at random, then the probability that the point is in region B, which is in the interior of region A, is $\frac{\text{area of region } B}{\text{area of region } A}$.

Example: Suppose a dart is thrown at random at a circular dartboard like the one shown at the right and hits the dartboard. What is the probability that the dart will land in the bullseye?

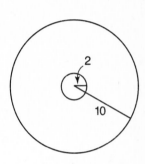

Area of bullseye: $A = \pi(2)^2$
$A = 4\pi$

Area of entire dartboard: $A = \pi(10)^2$
$A = 100\pi$

Probability of bullseye $= \frac{\text{area of bullseye}}{\text{area of dartboard}} = \frac{4\pi}{100\pi} = \frac{1}{25}$

Find the probability that a point chosen at random on $\overline{AH}$ is also a part of each of the following segments. Assume the twelve shortest segments are all congruent.

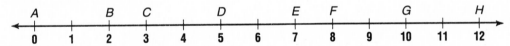

1. $\overline{AD}$ 2. $\overline{AE}$ 3. $\overline{DE}$ 4. $\overline{CG}$

Find the probability that a point chosen at random in each figure lies in the shaded region. Round your answers to the nearest hundredth.

5.
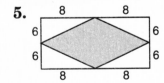

6.
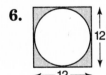

7.
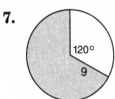

Study Guide

Integration: Probability
Geometric Probability

Geometric probability involves using length and area to find the probability of an event.

- If a point on $\overline{AB}$ is chosen at random and C is between A and B, then the probability that the point is on AC is $\frac{\text{length of } \overline{AC}}{\text{length of } \overline{AB}}$.

- If a point in region A is chosen at random, then the probability that the point is in region B, which is in the interior of region A, is $\frac{\text{area of region } B}{\text{area of region } A}$.

Example: Suppose a dart is thrown at random at a circular dartboard like the one shown at the right and hits the dartboard. What is the probability that the dart will land in the bullseye?

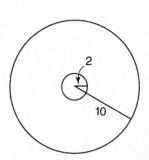

Area of bullseye: $A = \pi(2)^2$
$A = 4\pi$

Area of entire dartboard: $A = \pi(10)^2$
$A = 100\pi$

Probability of bullseye $= \frac{\text{area of bullseye}}{\text{area of dartboard}} = \frac{4\pi}{100\pi} = \frac{1}{25}$

Find the probability that a point chosen at random on $\overline{AH}$ is also a part of each of the following segments. Assume the twelve shortest segments are all congruent.

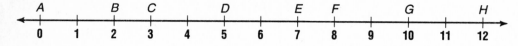

1. $\overline{AD}$ $\frac{5}{12}$
2. $\overline{AE}$ $\frac{7}{12}$
3. $\overline{DE}$ $\frac{1}{6}$
4. $\overline{CG}$ $\frac{7}{12}$

Find the probability that a point chosen at random in each figure lies in the shaded region. Round your answers to the nearest hundredth.

5.
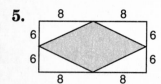

0.50

6.

0.21

7.
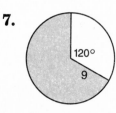

0.67

Study Guide

Integration: Graph Theory
Polygons As Networks

A network is a set of points called **nodes** that are connected by paths called **edges**. Often the nodes represent locations on a map and the edges represent connecting routes. The edges can be straight or curved. A network is **traceable** if you can trace it with your finger without lifting your finger or retracing an edge. A **complete** network is one with at least one edge between each pair of nodes.

The **degree** of a node is the number of edges connected to it. A network is traceable if and only if one of the following is true.

• All of the nodes in the network have even degrees.

• Exactly two nodes in the network have odd degrees.

Example: Determine if the network at the right is traceable.

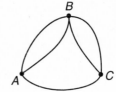

Node	Degree
A	3
B	4
C	3

The network is traceable.

Find the degree of each node in the network.

1.
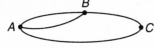

2.

3.
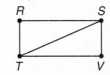

Determine if each network is traceable and complete. If a network is not complete, name the edges that need to be added to make the network complete.

4.

5.

6.

Determine whether each network is traceable.

7.

8.

9.

10–7

Study Guide

Integration: Graph Theory
Polygons As Networks

A network is a set of points called **nodes** that are connected by paths called **edges**. Often the nodes represent locations on a map and the edges represent connecting routes. The edges can be straight or curved. A network is **traceable** if you can trace it with your finger without lifting your finger or retracing an edge. A **complete** network is one with at least one edge between each pair of nodes.

The **degree** of a node is the number of edges connected to it. A network is traceable if and only if one of the following is true.

• All of the nodes in the network have even degrees.

• Exactly two nodes in the network have odd degrees.

Example: Determine if the network at the right is traceable.

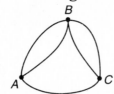

Node	Degree
A	3
B	4
C	3

The network is traceable.

Find the degree of each node in the network.

1.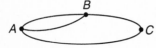

A-3, B-3, C-2

2.

D-3, E-1, F-2

3.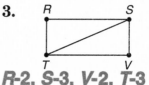

R-2, S-3, V-2, T-3

Determine if each network is traceable and complete. If a network is not complete, name the edges that need to be added to make the network complete.

4.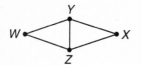

not complete; edge WX

5.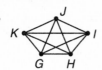

complete

6.

not complete; edges LM, MN, NP, PQ, QL

Determine whether each network is traceable.

7.

not traceable

8.

traceable

9.

traceable

Study Guide

Student Edition
Pages 575–581

Exploring Three-Dimensional Figures

Looking at a picture of a building does not allow you to determine its three-dimensional shape. Depth and the complete configuration of an object can be determined if the front, top, and side views of the object are provided.

Example: Various views of a solid figure are shown below. The edge of one block represents one unit of length. A dark segment indicates a break in the surface. To draw the back view of the figure, make a model based on the information given in the views below.

| top view | left view | front view | right view |

- The top view indicates that one column is taller than the other.
- The left view indicates the taller column is 3 blocks high while the shorter column is 2 blocks high, and is the closest column to you in this view.

This is the back view based on the model built from the information given.

Make a model of each figure. Then draw the back view of the figure.

| top view | left view | front view | right view |

1.

2.

3.

4.

Study Guide

Exploring Three-Dimensional Figures

Looking at a picture of a building does not allow you to determine its three-dimensional shape. Depth and the complete configuration of an object can be determined if the front, top, and side views of the object are provided.

Example: Various views of a solid figure are shown below. The edge of one block represents one unit of length. A dark segment indicates a break in the surface. To draw the back view of the figure, make a model based on the information given in the views below.

top view	left view	front view	right view

- The top view indicates that one column is taller than the other.
- The left view indicates the taller column is 3 blocks high while the shorter column is 2 blocks high, and is the closest column to you in this view.

This is the back view based on the model built from the information given.

Make a model of each figure. Then draw the back view of the figure.

	top view	left view	front view	right view	back view
1.					
2.					
3.					
4.					

Study Guide

Nets and Surface Area

The **surface area** of a three-dimensional object or solid is the sum of the areas of its outer surfaces. The surfaces that make up a polyhedron are polygons.

pyramid

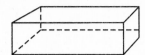

rectangular solid

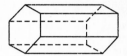

hexagonal solid

When a polyhedron is unfolded, the result is a two-dimensional figure called a **net**.

Example: Match the net at the right with one of the solids below.

a.   **b.**   **c.**

The net represents solid c.

Identify the number and type of polygons that are faces of each polyhedron.

1.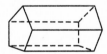

2.

3.

Given each polyhedron, copy its net and label the remaining vertices.

4.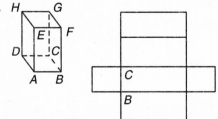

5.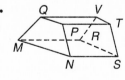

Study Guide

Nets and Surface Area

The **surface area** of a three-dimensional object or solid is the sum of the areas of its outer surfaces. The surfaces that make up a polyhedron are polygons.

pyramid

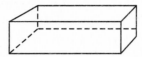

rectangular solid

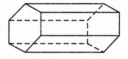

hexagonal solid

When a polyhedron is unfolded, the result is a two-dimensional figure called a **net**.

Example: Match the net at the right with one of the solids below.

a. 　　**b.** 　　**c.**

The net represents solid c.

Identify the number and type of polygons that are faces of each polyhedron.

1.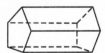

2.

3.

2 pentagons,
5 rectangles

1 rectangle,
4 triangles

6 triangles

Given each polyhedron, copy its net and label the remaining vertices.

4.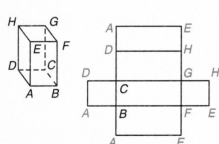

5.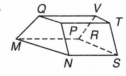

Study Guide

Surface Area of Prisms and Cylinders

Prisms are polyhedrons with congruent polygonal bases in parallel planes. **Cylinders** have congruent and parallel circular bases. An **altitude** is a perpendicular segment joining the planes of the bases. The length of an altitude is the **height** of the figure. **Right prisms** have lateral edges that are altitudes. A right cylinder is one whose **axis** is an altitude.

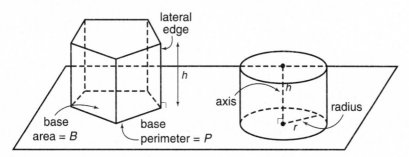

In the following formulas, L is lateral and T is total surface area.

Prisms $L = Ph$ **Cylinders** $L = 2\pi rh$
          $T = Ph + 2B$ $T = 2\pi rh + 2\pi r^2$

Example: Find the surface area of the right cylinder.

$T = 2\pi rh + 2\pi r^2$
$T = 2\pi(3.5)(6) + 2\pi(3.5)^2$
$T = 66.5\pi$ or about 208.92 cm^2

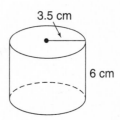

Find the lateral area and the surface area of each right prism or right cylinder. Round your answers to the nearest tenth.

1.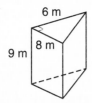

2.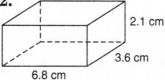

3.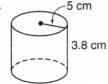

4.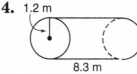

Study Guide

Surface Area of Prisms and Cylinders

Prisms are polyhedrons with congruent polygonal bases in parallel planes. **Cylinders** have congruent and parallel circular bases. An **altitude** is a perpendicular segment joining the planes of the bases. The length of an altitude is the **height** of the figure. **Right prisms** have lateral edges that are altitudes. A right cylinder is one whose **axis** is an altitude.

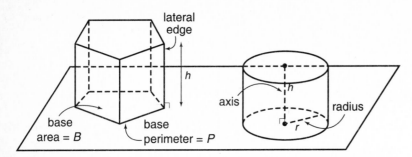

In the following formulas, L is lateral and T is total surface area.

Prisms $L = Ph$ **Cylinders** $L = 2\pi rh$
$\quad\quad\quad T = Ph + 2B$ $\quad\quad\quad\quad T = 2\pi rh + 2\pi r^2$

Example: Find the surface area of the right cylinder.

$T = 2\pi rh + 2\pi r^2$
$T = 2\pi(3.5)(6) + 2\pi(3.5)^2$
$T = 66.5\pi$ or about 208.92 cm^2

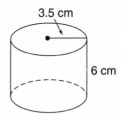

3.5 cm

6 cm

Find the lateral area and the surface area of each right prism or right cylinder. Round your answers to the nearest tenth.

1.
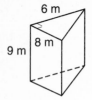
6 m
9 m   8 m

$L = 216$ m^2
$T = 264$ m^2

2.
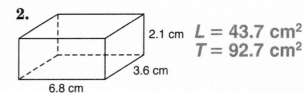
2.1 cm
3.6 cm
6.8 cm

$L = 43.7$ cm^2
$T = 92.7$ cm^2

3.
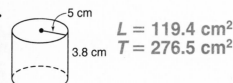
5 cm
3.8 cm

$L = 119.4$ cm^2
$T = 276.5$ cm^2

4.
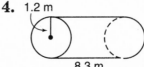
1.2 m
8.3 m

$L = 62.6$ m^2
$T = 71.6$ m^2

11-4

Study Guide

Surface Area of Pyramids and Cones

All the faces of a **pyramid**, except one, intersect at a point called the **vertex**. A pyramid is a **regular pyramid** if its base is a regular polygon and the segment from the vertex to the center of the base is perpendicular to the base. All the lateral faces of a regular pyramid are congruent isosceles triangles. The height of each lateral face is called the **slant height**.

The slant height of a right circular cone is the length of a segment from the vertex to the edge of the circular base.

In the following formulas, L is lateral area, T is total surface area, P is perimeter, and ℓ is slant height.

Regular Pyramids $L = \frac{1}{2}P\ell$
$T = \text{Lateral Area} + \text{Area of Base}$

Cones $L = \pi r\ell$
$T = \pi r\ell + \pi r^2$

Example: Find the surface area of the cone.

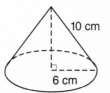

$T = \pi r\ell + \pi r^2$
$T = \pi(6)(10) + \pi(6)^2$
$T = 60\pi + 36\pi$
$T = 96\pi$ or about 301.6 cm

Find the lateral area and the surface area of each regular pyramid or right cone. Round your answers to the nearest tenth.

1.

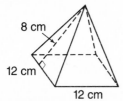

2.

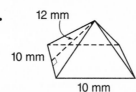

3.

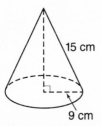

4.

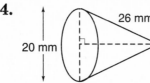

Study Guide

Surface Area of Pyramids and Cones

All the faces of a **pyramid**, except one, intersect at a point called the **vertex**. A pyramid is a **regular pyramid** if its base is a regular polygon and the segment from the vertex to the center of the base is perpendicular to the base. All the lateral faces of a regular pyramid are congruent isosceles triangles. The height of each lateral face is called the **slant height**.

The slant height of a right circular cone is the length of a segment from the vertex to the edge of the circular base.

In the following formulas, L is lateral area, T is total surface area, P is perimeter, and ℓ is slant height.

Regular Pyramids $L = \frac{1}{2}P\ell$
$T = \text{Lateral Area} + \text{Area of Base}$

Cones $L = \pi r\ell$
$T = \pi r\ell + \pi r^2$

Example: Find the surface area of the cone.

$T = \pi r\ell + \pi r^2$
$T = \pi(6)(10) + \pi(6)^2$
$T = 60\pi + 36\pi$
$T = 96\pi$ or about 301.6 cm

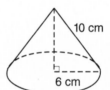

Find the lateral area and the surface area of each regular pyramid or right cone. Round your answers to the nearest tenth.

1.

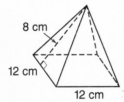

8 cm
12 cm
12 cm

$L = 192 \text{ cm}^2$
$T = 336 \text{ cm}^2$

2.

12 mm
10 mm
10 mm

$L = 240 \text{ mm}^2$
$T = 340 \text{ mm}^2$

3.

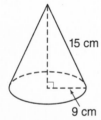

15 cm
9 cm

$L = 424.1 \text{ cm}^2$
$T = 678.6 \text{ cm}^2$

4.

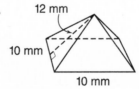

26 mm
20 mm

$L = 816.8 \text{ mm}^2$
$T = 1131.0 \text{ mm}^2$

NAME_____ DATE _____

Study Guide

Student Edition
Pages 607–613

Volume of Prisms and Cylinders

The measure of the amount of space that a figure encloses is the **volume** of the figure. Volume is measured in cubic units such as cubic yards or cubic feet. A cubic foot is equivalent to a cube that is 1 foot long on each side. A cubic yard is equivalent to 27 cubic feet.

cubic foot

cubic yard

Volume of a Right Prism	If a right prism has a volume of V cubic units, a base of B square units, and a height of h units, then $V = Bh$.
Volume of a Right Cylinder	If a right cylinder has a volume of V cubic units, a height of h units, and a radius of r units, then $V = \pi r^2 h$.

Examples: Find the volume of each right prism or right cylinder.

1
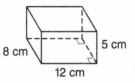
8 cm   5 cm
12 cm

2
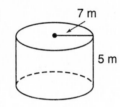
7 m
5 m

$V = Bh$
$V = (8)(12)(5)$
$V = 480 \text{ cm}^3$

$V = \pi r^2 h$
$V = \pi (7)^2 (5)$
$V = 245\pi$ or about 769.7 m³

Find the volume of each right prism or right cylinder. Round your answers to the nearest tenth.

1.
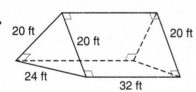
20 ft   20 ft   20 ft
24 ft
32 ft

2.
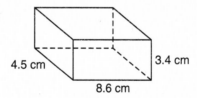
4.5 cm   3.4 cm
8.6 cm

3.
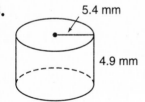
5.4 mm
4.9 mm

4.
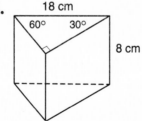
18 cm
60°   30°
8 cm

Geometry

Study Guide

Volume of Prisms and Cylinders

The measure of the amount of space that a figure encloses is the **volume** of the figure. Volume is measured in cubic units such as cubic yards or cubic feet. A cubic foot is equivalent to a cube that is 1 foot long on each side. A cubic yard is equivalent to 27 cubic feet.

cubic foot

cubic yard

Volume of a Right Prism	If a right prism has a volume of V cubic units, a base of B square units, and a height of h units, then $V = Bh$.
Volume of a Right Cylinder	If a right cylinder has a volume of V cubic units, a height of h units, and a radius of r units, then $V = \pi r^2 h$.

Examples: Find the volume of each right prism or right cylinder.

1

8 cm · 12 cm · 5 cm

$V = Bh$
$V = (8)(12)(5)$
$V = 480 \text{ cm}^3$

2

7 m · 5 m

$V = \pi r^2 h$
$V = \pi (7)^2 (5)$
$V = 245\pi$ or about 769.7 m^3

Find the volume of each right prism or right cylinder. Round your answers to the nearest tenth.

1.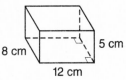

20 ft · 20 ft · 20 ft · 20 ft · 24 ft · 32 ft

6144.0 ft³

2.

4.5 cm · 3.4 cm · 8.6 cm

131.6 cm³

3.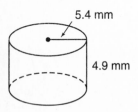

5.4 mm · 4.9 mm

448.9 mm³

4.

18 cm · 60° · 30° · 8 cm

561.2 cm³

11–6

Study Guide

Volume of Pyramids and Cones

Volume of a Right Circular Cone	If a right circular cone has a volume of V cubic units, a height of h units, and the area of the base is B units, then $V = \frac{1}{3} Bh$
Volume of a Right Pyramid	If a right pyramid has a volume of V cubic units, a height of h units, and the area of the base is B square units, then $V = \frac{1}{3} Bh$.

Examples: Find the volume of each solid.

1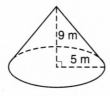

$$V = \frac{1}{3}Bh$$
$$V = \frac{1}{3}\pi (5^2)(9)$$
$$V = 75\pi \text{ or about } 235.6 \text{ m}^3$$

2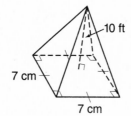

$$V = \frac{1}{3}Bh$$
$$V = \frac{1}{3}(49)\,10$$
$$V = \frac{490}{3} \text{ or about } 163.3 \text{ cm}^3$$

Find the volume of each solid. Round your answers to the nearest tenth.

1.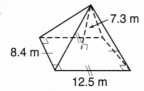

2.

3.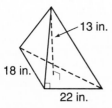

4.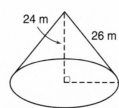

5.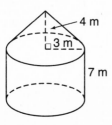

6.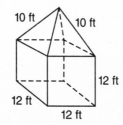

NAME_____ DATE _____

Study Guide

Volume of Pyramids and Cones

Volume of a Right Circular Cone	If a right circular cone has a volume of V cubic units, a height of h units, and the area of the base is B units, then $V = \frac{1}{3}Bh$
Volume of a Right Pyramid	If a right pyramid has a volume of V cubic units, a height of h units, and the area of the base is B square units, then $V = \frac{1}{3}Bh$.

Examples: Find the volume of each solid.

1
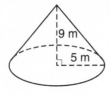

$$V = \frac{1}{3}Bh$$
$$V = \frac{1}{3}\pi(5^2)(9)$$
$$V = 75\pi \text{ or about } 235.6 \text{ m}^3$$

2
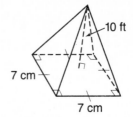

$$V = \frac{1}{3}Bh$$
$$V = \frac{1}{3}(49)\,10$$
$$V = \frac{490}{3} \text{ or about } 163.3 \text{ cm}^3$$

Find the volume of each solid. Round your answers to the nearest tenth.

1.
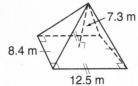
255.5 m³

2.

1187.5 ft³

3.
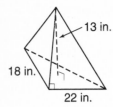
858 in³

4.
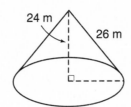
2513.3 m³

5.
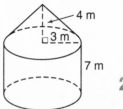
235.6 m³

6.
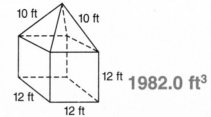
1982.0 ft³

NAME_____ DATE _____

Study Guide

Surface Area and Volume of Spheres

The following is a list of definitions related to the study of spheres.

Sphere   the set of all points that are a given distance from a given point (center)

Radius   a segment whose endpoints are the center of the sphere and a point on the sphere

Chord   a segment whose endpoints are points on the sphere

Diameter   a chord that contains the sphere's center

Tangent   a line that intersects the sphere in exactly one point

Great Circle   the intersection of a plane and a sphere so that the center of the sphere is included

Hemispheres   two congruent halves of a sphere separated by a great circle

Describe each object as a model of a _circle_, _sphere_, or _neither_.

1. tennis ball can   2. pancake   3. sun

4. basketball rim   5. globe   6. lipstick container

Determine whether each statement is _true_ or _false_.

7. All lines intersecting a sphere are tangent to the sphere.

8. Every plane that intersects a sphere creates a great circle.

9. The eastern hemisphere of Earth is congruent to the western hemisphere of Earth.

10. The diameter of a sphere is congruent to the diameter of its great circle.

Study Guide

Surface Area and Volume of Spheres

The following is a list of definitions related to the study of spheres.

Sphere	the set of all points that are a given distance from a given point (center)
Radius	a segment whose endpoints are the center of the sphere and a point on the sphere
Chord	a segment whose endpoints are points on the sphere
Diameter	a chord that contains the sphere's center
Tangent	a line that intersects the sphere in exactly one point
Great Circle	the intersection of a plane and a sphere so that the center of the sphere is included
Hemispheres	two congruent halves of a sphere separated by a great circle

Describe each object as a model of a _circle_, _sphere_, or _neither_.

1. tennis ball can
   neither

2. pancake
   circle

3. sun
   sphere

4. basketball rim
   circle

5. globe
   sphere

6. lipstick container
   neither

Determine whether each statement is _true_ or _false_.

7. All lines intersecting a sphere are tangent to the sphere. false

8. Every plane that intersects a sphere creates a great circle. false

9. The eastern hemisphere of Earth is congruent to the western hemisphere of Earth. true

10. The diameter of a sphere is congruent to the diameter of its great circle. true

NAME_____ DATE _____

Study Guide

Congruent and Similar Solids

Solids that have the same shape but are different in size are said to be **similar**. You can determine if two solids are similar by comparing the ratios **(scale factors)** of corresponding linear measurements. If the scale factor is 1:1, then the solids are **congruent**.

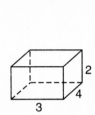 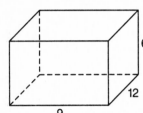

similar

 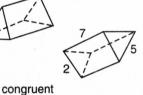

congruent

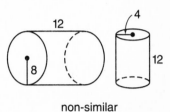

non-similar

Determine if each pair of solids is _similar_, _congruent_, or _neither_.

1.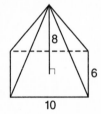

2.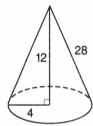

3.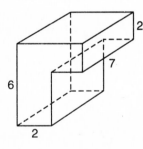

4.

5.

6.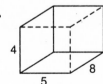

Student Edition
Pages 629–635

11–8

Study Guide

Congruent and Similar Solids

Solids that have the same shape but are different in size are said to be **similar**. You can determine if two solids are similar by comparing the ratios **(scale factors)** of corresponding linear measurements. If the scale factor is 1:1, then the solids are **congruent**.

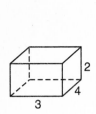 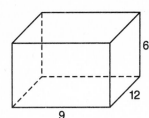

similar

congruent

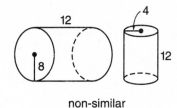

non-similar

Determine if each pair of solids is similar, congruent, or neither.

1.

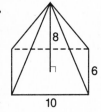

similar

2.

 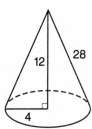

neither

3.

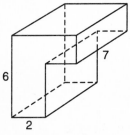 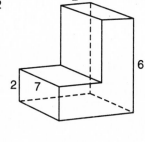

congruent

4.

similar

5.

neither

6.

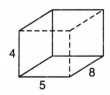

congruent

Geometry

NAME_____ DATE _____

Study Guide

Integration: Algebra
Graphing Linear Equations

One method for graphing a linear equation is called the **intercepts method**. The **x-intercept** is the value of x when $y = 0$. The **y-intercept** is the value of y when $x = 0$. By plotting the points on the axes that correspond to the intercepts, you can then draw the line for the equation. (This method will not work if the line is parallel to either axis.)

When an equation is written in the form $y = mx + b$, the equation is said to be in **slope-intercept form**, where m is the slope of the line and b is the y-intercept. The graph of an equation of the form $x = a$ is a vertical line and has an undefined slope. The graph of an equation of the form $y = b$ is a horizontal line and has a slope of 0.

Example: Graph $y = \frac{2}{3}x + 4$ using the slope and the y-intercept.

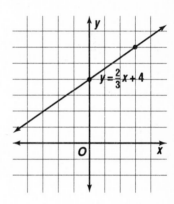

Since the equation is in slope-intercept form, the slope is $\frac{2}{3}$ and the y-intercept is 4.

Plot the point with coordinates (0, 4). From this point move up 2 units and to the right 3 units. The point at (3, 6) must also lie on the line.

Find the x- and y-intercepts and slope of the graph of each equation.

1. $6x + 4y = -24$ **2.** $y + 5 = x$ **3.** $x = 5$

Graph each equation.

4. $3x - 6y = 12$ **5.** $2x + y = 3$ **6.** $y + 4x = 2$

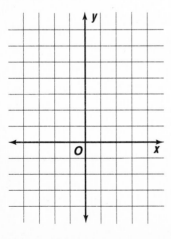   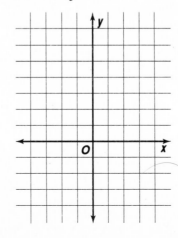   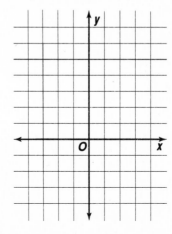

Study Guide

Integration: Algebra
Graphing Linear Equations

One method for graphing a linear equation is called the **intercepts method**. The **x-intercept** is the value of x when $y = 0$. The **y-intercept** is the value of y when $x = 0$. By plotting the points on the axes that correspond to the intercepts, you can then draw the line for the equation. (This method will not work if the line is parallel to either axis.)

When an equation is written in the form $y = mx + b$, the equation is said to be in **slope-intercept form**, where m is the slope of the line and b is the y-intercept. The graph of an equation of the form $x = a$ is a vertical line and has an undefined slope. The graph of an equation of the form $y = b$ is a horizontal line and has a slope of 0.

Example: Graph $y = \frac{2}{3}x + 4$ using the slope and the y-intercept.

Since the equation is in slope-intercept form, the slope is $\frac{2}{3}$ and the y-intercept is 4.

Plot the point with coordinates $(0, 4)$. From this point move up 2 units and to the right 3 units. The point at $(3, 6)$ must also lie on the line.

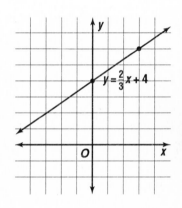

Find the x- and y-intercepts and slope of the graph of each equation.

1. $6x + 4y = -24$
$-4, -6, m = -\frac{3}{2}$

2. $y + 5 = x$
$4, -5, m = 1$

3. $x = 5$
5, no y-intercept, m is undefined

Graph each equation.

4. $3x - 6y = 12$

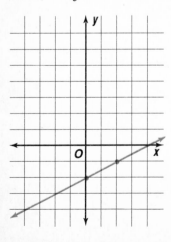

5. $2x + y = 3$

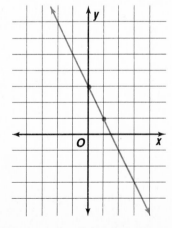

6. $y + 4x = 2$

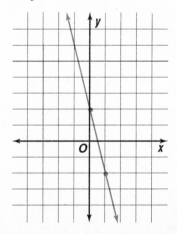

Study Guide

Integration: Algebra
Writing Equations of Lines

You can write an equation of a line if you are given
- the slope and the coordinates of a point on the line, or
- the coordinates of two points on the line.

Example: Write the equation in slope-intercept form of the line that has slope 5 and an x-intercept of 3.

Since the slope is 5, you can substitute 5 for m in $y = mx + b$.
$y = 5x + b$

Since the x-intercept is 3, the point $(3, 0)$ is on the line.
$y = 5x + b$
$0 = 5(3) + b$ **$y = 0$ and $x = 3$**
$0 = 15 + b$
$b = -15$ **Solve for b.**
So the equation is $y = 5x - 15$.

If you know two points on a line, you will need to use the point-slope form of the equation, that is, $y - y_1 = m(x - x_1)$.

Write the equation in slope-intercept form of the line that satisfies the given conditions.

1. $m = 3$, y-intercept $= -4$

2. $m = -\frac{2}{5}$, x-intercept $= 6$

3. passes through $(-5, 10)$ and $(2, 4)$

4. passes through $(8, 6)$ and $(-3, -3)$

5. perpendicular to the y-axis, passes through $(-6, 4)$

6. parallel to the y-axis, passes through $(-7, 3)$

7. $m = 3$ and passes through $(-4, 6)$

8. perpendicular to the graph of $y = 4x - 1$ and passes through $(6, -3)$

12-2

Study Guide

Integration: Algebra
Writing Equations of Lines

You can write an equation of a line if you are given
- the slope and the coordinates of a point on the line, or
- the coordinates of two points on the line.

Example: Write the equation in slope-intercept form of the line that has slope 5 and an x-intercept of 3.

Since the slope is 5, you can substitute 5 for m in $y = mx + b$.
$y = 5x + b$

Since the x-intercept is 3, the point (3, 0) is on the line.
$y = 5x + b$
$0 = 5(3) + b$ **$y = 0$ and $x = 3$**
$0 = 15 + b$
$b = -15$ **Solve for b.**

So the equation is $y = 5x - 15$.

If you know two points on a line, you will need to use the point-slope form of the equation, that is, $y - y_1 = m(x - x_1)$.

Write the equation in slope-intercept form of the line that satisfies the given conditions.

1. $m = 3$, y-intercept $= -4$
$y = 3x - 4$

2. $m = -\frac{2}{5}$, x-intercept $= 6$
$y = -\frac{2}{5}x + \frac{12}{5}$

3. passes through $(-5, 10)$ and $(2, 4)$
$y = -\frac{6}{7}x + \frac{40}{7}$

4. passes through $(8, 6)$ and $(-3, -3)$
$y = \frac{9}{11}x - \frac{6}{11}$

5. perpendicular to the y-axis, passes through $(-6, 4)$
$y = 4$

6. parallel to the y-axis, passes through $(-7, 3)$
$x = -7$

7. $m = 3$ and passes through $(-4, 6)$

$y = 3x + 18$

8. perpendicular to the graph of $y = 4x - 1$ and passes through $(6, -3)$
$y = -\frac{1}{4}x - \frac{3}{2}$

    T73   *Geometry*

12-3

Study Guide

Integration: Algebra and Statistics
Scatter Plots and Slope

The methods you have learned for writing equations of lines are helpful when applied to geometric concepts. For example, when you are given the coordinates of the vertices for a triangle, you can use these coordinates to find the equations of various lines, such as the lines that contain the altitudes, medians, or perpendicular bisectors.

Example: The vertices of $\triangle ABC$ are $A(0, 12)$, $B(-6, 6)$, and $C(4, 8)$. Write the equation of the line containing the perpendicular bisector of $\overline{BC}$.

The midpoint of $\overline{BC}$ is $\left(\dfrac{-6+4}{2}, \dfrac{6+8}{2}\right)$ or $(-1, 7)$.

Slope of $\overline{BC} = \dfrac{8-6}{4-(-6)} = \dfrac{2}{10} = \dfrac{1}{5}$

So the perpendicular bisector of $\overline{BC}$ must have a slope of -5.

Since you know the slope of the perpendicular bisector and one point on it, you can write the equation.

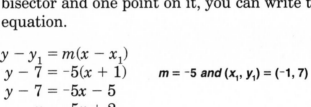

$y - y_1 = m(x - x_1)$
$y - 7 = -5(x + 1)$ *m = -5 and (x₁, y₁) = (-1, 7)*
$y - 7 = -5x - 5$
$y = -5x + 2$

The vertices of $\triangle RST$ are R(0, 10), S(-5, 0) and T(5, 5). Write in slope-intercept form the equations of the lines that contain the segments described.

1. the sides of $\triangle RST$

2. the medians of $\triangle RST$

3. the altitudes of $\triangle RST$

4. the perpendicular bisectors of $\triangle RST$

NAME_____ DATE _____

Study Guide

Integration: Algebra and Statistics
Scatter Plots and Slope

The methods you have learned for writing equations of lines are helpful when applied to geometric concepts. For example, when you are given the coordinates of the vertices for a triangle, you can use these coordinates to find the equations of various lines, such as the lines that contain the altitudes, medians, or perpendicular bisectors.

Example: The vertices of $\triangle ABC$ are $A(0, 12)$, $B(-6, 6)$, and $C(4, 8)$. Write the equation of the line containing the perpendicular bisector of $\overline{BC}$.

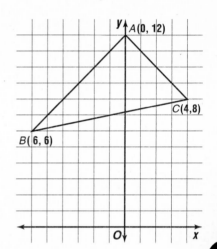

The midpoint of $\overline{BC}$ is $\left(\dfrac{-6+4}{2}, \dfrac{6+8}{2}\right)$ or $(-1, 7)$.

Slope of $\overline{BC} = \dfrac{8-6}{4-(-6)} = \dfrac{2}{10} = \dfrac{1}{5}$

So the perpendicular bisector of $\overline{BC}$ must have a slope of -5.

Since you know the slope of the perpendicular bisector and one point on it, you can write the equation.

$y - y_1 = m(x - x_1)$
$y - 7 = -5(x + 1)$ $m = -5$ and $(x_1, y_1) = (-1, 7)$
$y - 7 = -5x - 5$
$y = -5x + 2$

The vertices of $\triangle RST$ are $R(0, 10)$, $S(-5, 0)$ and $T(5, 5)$. Write in slope-intercept form the equations of the lines that contain the segments described.

1. the sides of $\triangle RST$
$y = 2x + 10$
$y = -x + 10$
$y = \dfrac{1}{2}x + \dfrac{5}{2}$

2. the medians of $\triangle RST$
$x = 0$
$y = x + 5$
$y = 5$

3. the altitudes of $\triangle RST$
$y = -2x + 10$
$y = -\dfrac{1}{2}x + \dfrac{15}{2}$
$y = x + 5$

4. the perpendicular bisectors of $\triangle RST$
$y = -2x + \dfrac{5}{2}$
$y = -\dfrac{1}{2}x + \dfrac{15}{4}$
$y = x + 5$

          Geometry

NAME _____ DATE _____

Study Guide

Coordinate Proof

You can place figures in the coordinate plane and use algebra to prove theorems. The following guidelines for positioning figures can help keep the algebra simple.

- Use the origin as a vertex or center.
- Place at least one side of a polygon on an axis.
- Keep the figure within the first quadrant if possible.
- Use coordinates that make computations simple.

The distance formula, the midpoint formula, and your knowledge of slopes are useful tools for coordinate proofs.

Example: Use a coordinate proof to prove that the diagonals of a rectangle are congruent.

Use (0, 0) as one vertex. Place another vertex on the x-axis at $(a, 0)$ and another on the y-axis at $(0, b)$. The fourth vertex must then be (a, b).

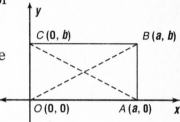

Use the distance formula to find OB and AC.

$$OB = \sqrt{(a-0)^2 + (b-0)^2} = \sqrt{a^2 + b^2}$$
$$AC = \sqrt{(0-a)^2 + (b-0)^2} = \sqrt{a^2 + b^2}$$

Since $OB = AC$, the diagonals are congruent.

Name the missing coordinates in terms of the given variables.

1. $ABCD$ is a rectangle.

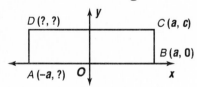

2. $HIJK$ is a parallelogram.

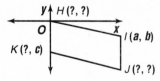

3. Use a coordinate proof to show that the opposite sides of any parallelogram are congruent.

y   C(b, c)   D(a + b, c)

O   A(0, 0)   B(a, 0)   *x*

Coordinate Proof

You can place figures in the coordinate plane and use algebra to prove theorems. The following guidelines for positioning figures can help keep the algebra simple.

- Use the origin as a vertex or center.
- Place at least one side of a polygon on an axis.
- Keep the figure within the first quadrant if possible.
- Use coordinates that make computations simple.

The distance formula, the midpoint formula, and your knowledge of slopes are useful tools for coordinate proofs.

Example: Use a coordinate proof to prove that the diagonals of a rectangle are congruent.

Use (0, 0) as one vertex. Place another vertex on the x-axis at $(a, 0)$ and another on the y-axis at $(0, b)$. The fourth vertex must then be (a, b).

Use the distance formula to find OB and AC.

$$OB = \sqrt{(a - 0)^2 + (b - 0)^2} = \sqrt{a^2 + b^2}$$
$$AC = \sqrt{(0 - a)^2 + (b - 0)^2} = \sqrt{a^2 + b^2}$$

Since $OB = AC$, the diagonals are congruent.

Name the missing coordinates in terms of the given variables.

1. $ABCD$ is a rectangle.

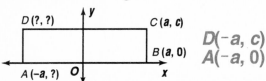

$D(-a, c)$
$A(-a, 0)$

2. $HIJK$ is a parallelogram.

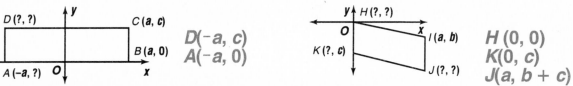

$H(0, 0)$
$K(0, c)$
$J(a, b + c)$

3. Use a coordinate proof to show that the opposite sides of any parallelogram are congruent. Label the vertices $A(0, 0)$, $B(a, 0)$, $C(b, c)$, and $D(a + b, c)$. Then use the distance formula to find AB, CD, AC, and BD.

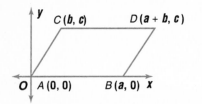

$$AB = \sqrt{(a + 0)^2 + (0 - 0)^2} = \sqrt{a^2} = a$$
$$CD = \sqrt{((a + b) - b)^2 + (c - c)^2} = \sqrt{a^2} = a$$
$$BD = \sqrt{((a + b) - a)^2 + (c - 0)^2} = \sqrt{b^2 + c^2}$$
$$AC = \sqrt{(b - 0)^2 + (c - 0)^2} = \sqrt{b^2 + c^2}$$

So $AB = CD$ and $AC = BD$. Therefore, the opposite sides of a parallelogram are congruent.

NAME_____ DATE _____

Study Guide

Vectors

A **vector** is any quantity that has both **magnitude** (length) and **direction**. In symbols, a vector is written as $\vec{v}$ or $\overrightarrow{AB}$. Vectors with the initial point at (0, 0) can be represented by the ordered pair for point B. You can write $\vec{v} = (5, 3)$.

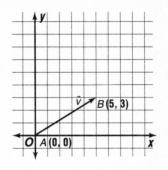

You can use the distance formula to find the magnitude of a vector. The symbol for the magnitude of $\overrightarrow{AB}$ is $|\overrightarrow{AB}|$. The direction of a vector is the measure of the angle that the vector forms with the positive x-axis or any other horizontal line. Equal vectors are vectors with the same magnitude and direction.

Example: Given $A(5, 2)$ and $B(8, 7)$, find the magnitude and direction of AB.

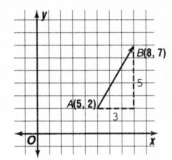

Magnitude
$$|\overrightarrow{AB}| = \sqrt{(8-5)^2 + (7-2)^2}$$
$$= \sqrt{34} \text{ or about 5.8 units}$$

Direction
$\tan A = \dfrac{5}{3}$ $\tan A = \dfrac{\text{opposite}}{\text{adjacent}}$
$m\angle A \approx 59.0$

The magnitude is about 5.8 units, and the direction is about 59°.

To find the **resultant** or sum of two vectors, you can represent them by equal vectors with initial points at (0, 0) and then add corresponding coordinates.

For each vector, find the magnitude to the nearest tenth and the direction to the nearest degree.

1. $\vec{v} = (8, 2)$

2. $\overrightarrow{AB}$ if $A(3, 0)$ and $B(5, 7)$

Given $\vec{a} = (4, 6)$ and $\vec{b} = (9, -4)$, represent each of the following as an ordered pair.

3. $\vec{a} + 2\vec{b}$

4. $\vec{a} - \vec{b}$

5. $2\vec{a} - \vec{b}$

6. $3\vec{a} + (\vec{a} - \vec{b})$

Study Guide

Vectors

A **vector** is any quantity that has both **magnitude** (length) and **direction**. In symbols, a vector is written as $\vec{v}$ or $\overrightarrow{AB}$. Vectors with the initial point at (0, 0) can be represented by the ordered pair for point B. You can write $\vec{v} = (5, 3)$.

You can use the distance formula to find the magnitude of a vector. The symbol for the magnitude of $\overrightarrow{AB}$ is $|\overrightarrow{AB}|$. The direction of a vector is the measure of the angle that the vector forms with the positive x-axis or any other horizontal line. Equal vectors are vectors with the same magnitude and direction.

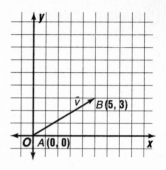

Example: Given $A(5, 2)$ and $B(8, 7)$, find the magnitude and direction of AB.

Magnitude
$$|\overrightarrow{AB}| = \sqrt{(8 - 5)^2 + (7 - 2)^2}$$
$$= \sqrt{34} \text{ or about 5.8 units}$$

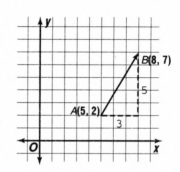

Direction
$$\tan A = \frac{5}{3} \qquad \tan A = \frac{\text{opposite}}{\text{adjacent}}$$
$$m\angle A \approx 59.0$$

The magnitude is about 5.8 units, and the direction is about 59°.

To find the **resultant** or sum of two vectors, you can represent them by equal vectors with initial points at (0, 0) and then add corresponding coordinates.

For each vector, find the magnitude to the nearest tenth and the direction to the nearest degree.

1. $\vec{v} = (8, 2)$
   $\sqrt{68} \approx 8.2, 14°$

2. $\overrightarrow{AB}$ if $A(3, 0)$ and $B(5, 7)$
   $\sqrt{53} \approx 7.3, 74°$

Given $\vec{a} = (4, 6)$ and $\vec{b} = (9, \text{-}4)$, represent each of the following as an ordered pair.

3. $\vec{a} + 2\vec{b}$ (22, –2)

4. $\vec{a} - \vec{b}$ (–5, 10)

5. $2\vec{a} - \vec{b}$ (–1, 16)

6. $3\vec{a} + (\vec{a} - \vec{b})$ (7, 28)

Geometry

NAME _____ DATE _____

Study Guide

Coordinates in Space

In space, you need an **ordered triple** of real numbers to describe the location of a point. In space, the x-, y-, and z-axes are perpendicular to each other. In the figure at the right, the ordered triple $(-2, -3, 1)$ locates point P.

Given two points $A(x_1, y_1, z_1)$ and $B(x_2, y_2, z_2)$ in space, the distance between A and B is given by the following equation.

$$AB = \sqrt{(x_2 - x_1)^2 + (y_2 - y_1)^2 + (z_2 - z_1)^2}$$

The midpoint of $\overline{AB}$ has coordinates $\left(\dfrac{x_1 + x_2}{2}, \dfrac{y_1 + y_2}{2}, \dfrac{z_1 + z_2}{2}\right)$.

Example: Find AB given $A\,(3, 2, -5)$ and $B(-4, 6, 9)$. Then find the coordinates of the midpoint of $\overline{AB}$.

$$AB = \sqrt{(-4 - 3)^2 + (6 - 2)^2 + (9 - (-5))^2}$$

$$AB = \sqrt{(-7)^2 + (4)^2 + (14)^2}$$

$$AB = \sqrt{49 + 16 + 196}$$

$$AB = \sqrt{261} \approx 16.2$$

$$\text{midpoint of } \overline{AB} = \left(\frac{3 + (-4)}{2}, \frac{2 + 6}{2}, \frac{-5 + 9}{2}\right) = \left(-\frac{1}{2}, 4, 2\right)$$

Plot each point in a three-dimensional coordinate system.

1. $S(0, 4, 2)$

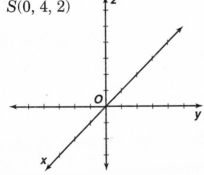

2. $T(5, -3, 6)$

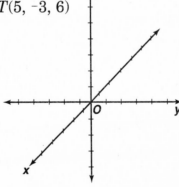

Determine the distance between each pair of points.

3. $A(0, 7, -4)$ and $B(-2, 8, 3)$

4. $C(-7, 6, 5)$ and $D(10, 2, -5)$

Determine the coordinates of the midpoint of each line segment whose endpoints are given.

5. $E(6, 10, -8)$ and $F(1, 20, 8)$

6. $G(0, -8, 4)$ and $H(8, 4, 3)$

Coordinates in Space

In space, you need an **ordered triple** of real numbers to describe the location of a point. In space, the x-, y-, and z-axes are perpendicular to each other. In the figure at the right, the ordered triple $(-2, -3, 1)$ locates point P.

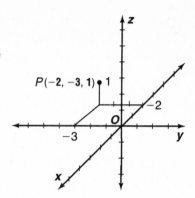

Given two points $A(x_1, y_1, z_1)$ and $B(x_2, y_2, z_2)$ in space, the distance between A and B is given by the following equation.

$$AB = \sqrt{(x_2 - x_1)^2 + (y_2 - y_1)^2 + (z_2 - z_1)^2}$$

The midpoint of $\overline{AB}$ has coordinates $\left(\frac{x_1 + x_2}{2}, \frac{y_1 + y_2}{2}, \frac{z_1 + z_2}{2}\right)$.

Example: Find AB given $A(3, 2, -5)$ and $B(-4, 6, 9)$. Then find the coordinates of the midpoint of $\overline{AB}$.

$$AB = \sqrt{(-4 - 3)^2 + (6 - 2)^2 + (9 - (-5))^2}$$

$$AB = \sqrt{(-7)^2 + (4)^2 + (14)^2}$$

$$AB = \sqrt{49 + 16 + 196}$$

$$AB = \sqrt{261} \approx 16.2$$

$$\text{midpoint of } \overline{AB} = \left(\frac{3 + (-4)}{2}, \frac{2 + 6}{2}, \frac{-5 + 9}{2}\right) = \left(-\frac{1}{2}, 4, 2\right)$$

Plot each point in a three-dimensional coordinate system.

1. $S(0, 4, 2)$

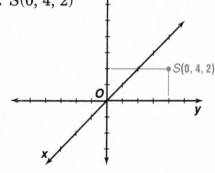

2. $T(5, -3, 6)$

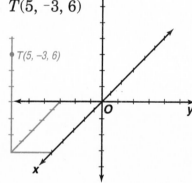

Determine the distance between each pair of points.

3. $A(0, 7, -4)$ and $B(-2, 8, 3)$
$\sqrt{54} \approx 7.3$

4. $C(-7, 6, 5)$ and $D(10, 2, -5)$
$\sqrt{405} \approx 20.1$

Determine the coordinates of the midpoint of each line segment whose endpoints are given.

5. $E(6, 10, -8)$ and $F(1, 20, 8)$ $\left(\frac{7}{2}, 15, 0\right)$

6. $G(0, -8, 4)$ and $H(8, 4, 3)$ $\left(4, -2, \frac{7}{2}\right)$

NAME _____ DATE _____

Study Guide

Student Edition
Pages 696–701

What Is Locus?

A **locus** is the set of all points that satisfy a given condition or set of conditions. In determining a locus, it is often helpful to draw a figure showing several points that meet the given conditions. Remember that the locus is the set of *all* points meeting the conditions. Be sure that your final figure includes all possibilities. Also be careful to note whether you are considering all points in space or only points in a plane.

Example: Describe the locus of points in a plane that are 1 inch from a circle with a radius of 5 inches.

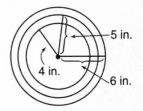

The locus consists of two circles having the same center as the 5-inch circle. One has a radius of 4 inches and the other has a radius of 6 inches.

Draw a figure and describe the locus of points that satisfy each set of conditions.

1. all points in a plane equidistant from two parallel lines that are 3 cm apart

2. all points in a plane that are 18 mm from a given point

3. all points in a plane that are less than 5 centimeters from a given point *P*

4. all points in a plane that are equidistant from the sides of the angle and not outside the angle

5. all points in space 2 inches from a given point

6. all points in space 2 inches from a given plane

What Is Locus?

A **locus** is the set of all points that satisfy a given condition or set of conditions. In determining a locus, it is often helpful to draw a figure showing several points that meet the given conditions. Remember that the locus is the set of *all* points meeting the conditions. Be sure that your final figure includes all possibilities. Also be careful to note whether you are considering all points in space or only points in a plane.

Example: Describe the locus of points in a plane that are 1 inch from a circle with a radius of 5 inches.

The locus consists of two circles having the same center as the 5-inch circle. One has a radius of 4 inches and the other has a radius of 6 inches.

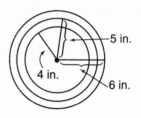

Draw a figure and describe the locus of points that satisfy each set of conditions.

1. all points in a plane equidistant from two parallel lines that are 3 cm apart

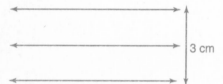

a line parallel to the two
parallel lines and halfway
between them

2. all points in a plane that are 18 mm from a given point

a circle with an 18 mm
radius and the given point
as center

3. all points in a plane that are less than 5 centimeters from a given point P

all interior points for the circle
of radius 5 cm and center P

4. all points in a plane that are equidistant from the sides of the angle and not outside the angle

the angle bisector

5. all points in space 2 inches from a given point

a sphere with a radius of
2 inches and having the
given point as center

6. all points in space 2 inches from a given plane

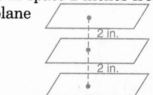

two planes parallel to the given
plane and 2 inches from either
side of it

13-2

Study Guide

Student Edition
Pages 702–708

Locus and Systems of Linear Equations

The graph of a linear equation in x and y is a straight line. Two linear equations form a **system of equations**. The locus of points that satisfy both equations of a system can be found graphically or algebraically. Two frequently used algebraic methods are the **substitution method** and the **elimination method**.

Example: Find the locus of points that satisfy both equations at the right by using both the substitution method and the elimination method.

$$2x - y = 3$$
$$3x + 2y = 22$$

Substitution Method

Solve the first equation for y in terms of x.

$$2x - y = 3$$
$$y = 2x - 3$$

Substitute $2x - 3$ for y in the second equation and solve for x.

$$3x + 2(2x - 3) = 22$$
$$3x + 4x - 6 = 22$$
$$7x = 28$$
$$x = 4$$

Find y by substituting 4 for x in the first equation.

$$2(4) - y = 3$$
$$8 - y = 3$$
$$y = 5$$

Elimination Method

$$2x - y = 3 \quad \blacktriangleleft \text{ Multiply by 2.}$$
$$3x + 2y = 22$$

$$4x - 2y = 6$$
$$\underline{3x + 2y = 22} \quad \blacktriangleleft \text{ Add to eliminate } y.$$
$$7x \quad\quad = 28$$
$$x = 4$$

Substitute 4 for x in the first equation. Solve for y.

$$2(4) - y = 3$$
$$y = 5$$

The point with coordinates (4, 5) is the locus of points that satisfy both equations.

State the locus of points that satisfy the intersection of each pair of lines.

1. a and b
2. a and c
3. b and c
4. a and d

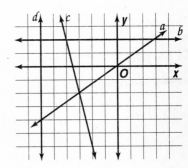

Use either substitution or elimination to find the locus of points that satisfy both equations.

5. $y = 7x + 1$
   $6x + y = 27$

6. $3x + y = 7$
   $2x - 3y = 12$

7. $3x + 4y = 36$
   $2x - 3y = -10$

NAME _____ DATE _____

Study Guide

Locus and Systems of Linear Equations

The graph of a linear equation in x and y is a straight line. Two linear equations form a **system of equations**. The locus of points that satisfy both equations of a system can be found graphically or algebraically. Two frequently used algebraic methods are the **substitution method** and the **elimination method**.

Example: Find the locus of points that satisfy both equations at the right by using both the substitution method and the elimination method.

$$2x - y = 3$$
$$3x + 2y = 22$$

Substitution Method

Solve the first equation for y in terms of x.

$2x - y = 3$
$\quad y = 2x - 3$

Substitute $2x - 3$ for y in the second equation and solve for x.

$3x + 2(2x - 3) = 22$
$\quad 3x + 4x - 6 = 22$
$\qquad\qquad 7x = 28$
$\qquad\qquad\; x = 4$

Find y by substituting 4 for x in the first equation.

$2(4) - y = 3$
$\quad 8 - y = 3$
$\qquad\; y = 5$

Elimination Method

$2x - y = 3$ ◄ Multiply by 2.
$3x + 2y = 22$

$4x - 2y = 6$
$\underline{3x + 2y = 22}$ ◄ Add to eliminate y.
$7x \qquad = 28$
$\quad x = 4$

Substitute 4 for x in the first equation. Solve for y.

$2(4) - y = 3$
$\qquad y = 5$

The point with coordinates (4, 5) is the locus of points that satisfy both equations.

State the locus of points that satisfy the intersection of each pair of lines.

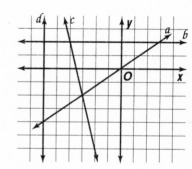

1. a and b **(3, 2)**
2. a and c **(−3, −2)**
3. b and c **(−4, 2)**
4. a and d **(−6, −4)**

Use either substitution or elimination to find the locus of points that satisfy both equations.

5. $y = 7x + 1$
   $6x + y = 27$
   (2, 15)

6. $3x + y = 7$
   $2x - 3y = 12$
   (3, −2)

7. $3x + 4y = 36$
   $2x - 3y = -10$
   (4, 6)

Study Guide

Intersection of Loci

Sometimes locus problems involve sets of points that satisfy
more than one set of conditions. In these cases, it is helpful to
draw a figure for each set of conditions and then find the point
or points where the figures intersect.

Example: Describe the locus of points in a plane 4 cm
from a line and 6 cm from a point *P* on the
line.

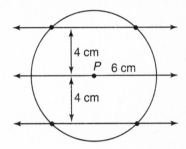

The locus of points 4 cm from the line is two
parallel lines, each one 4 cm from the given
line. The locus of points 6 cm from point *P* is a
circle with a radius 6 cm, with *P* its center.
The required locus consists of the 4 points
where the two parallel lines intersect the
circle.

**Draw a diagram to find the locus of points that satisfy the
conditions. Then describe the locus.**

1. all points in the coordinate plane
   that are 3 units from the graph of
   $x = 2$ and equidistant from the graphs
   $y = 1$ and $y = 5$

2. all the points in a plane that are
   10 cm from a given line and 12 cm
   from a given point *P* on the line

3. all interior points of an angle that
   are equidistant from the sides of the
   angle and 2 cm from the vertex of the
   angle

4. all points in space that are 5 inches
   from a given line and 4 inches from
   a given point on the line

NAME_____ DATE _____

Study Guide

Intersection of Loci

Sometimes locus problems involve sets of points that satisfy more than one set of conditions. In these cases, it is helpful to draw a figure for each set of conditions and then find the point or points where the figures intersect.

Example: Describe the locus of points in a plane 4 cm from a line and 6 cm from a point P on the line.

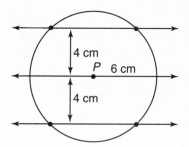

The locus of points 4 cm from the line is two parallel lines, each one 4 cm from the given line. The locus of points 6 cm from point P is a circle with a radius 6 cm, with P its center. The required locus consists of the 4 points where the two parallel lines intersect the circle.

Draw a diagram to find the locus of points that satisfy the conditions. Then describe the locus.

1. all points in the coordinate plane that are 3 units from the graph of $x = 2$ and equidistant from the graphs $y = 1$ and $y = 5$

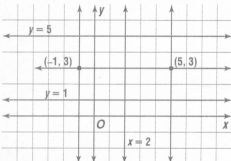

points (5, 3) and (−1, 3)

2. all the points in a plane that are 10 cm from a given line and 12 cm from a given point P on the line

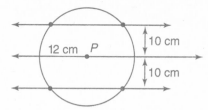

4 points at the intersection of a circle with a radius of 12 cm and 2 parallel lines each 10 cm from the given line

3. all interior points of an angle that are equidistant from the sides of the angle and 2 cm from the vertex of the angle

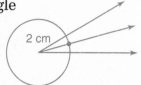

the point of intersection of the angle bisector and the circle of radius 2 cm with center at the vertex

4. all points in space that are 5 inches from a given line and 4 inches from a given point on the line

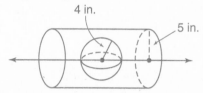

empty set

 Geometry

Study Guide

Mappings

A figure can be moved by any of the following methods:

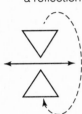

a reflection

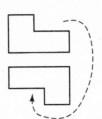

a rotation

a slide

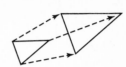

an enlargement or
reduction

In each case, each point (the **preimage**) of one figure is paired
with exactly one point (the **image**) of the corresponding figure.
This kind of one-to-one mapping is called a **transformation**.
The symbol → is used to indicate a mapping.

Example: If quadrilateral $ABCD \rightarrow$ quadrilateral $EFGH$,
name the preimage of each vertex of $EFGH$.

The preimages of E, F, G, and H
are A, B, C, and D.

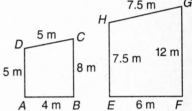

***Each figure below has a preimage or image of isometry. Write
the image of each given preimage.***

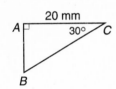
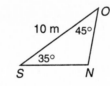
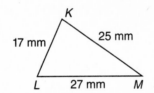
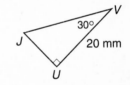

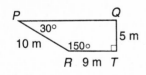
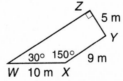
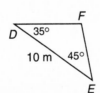
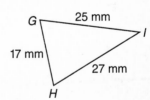

1. $\triangle ABC$

2. $\triangle DEF$

3. quadrilateral $XYZW$

4. $\triangle LMK$

5. $\triangle MKL$

6. quadrilateral $TRPQ$

7. Use a table of coordinates and the given figure to
determine the coordinates of the image after a
slide of 3 units up and a reflection across the
y-axis.

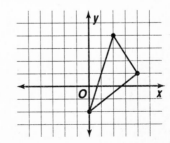

Study Guide

Mappings

A figure can be moved by any of the following methods:

 a reflection

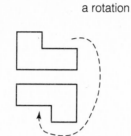 a rotation

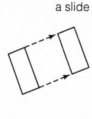 a slide

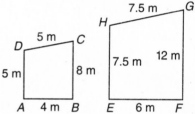 an enlargement or reduction

In each case, each point (the **preimage**) of one figure is paired with exactly one point (the **image**) of the corresponding figure. This kind of one-to-one mapping is called a **transformation**. The symbol → is used to indicate a mapping.

Example: If quadrilateral $ABCD$ → quadrilateral $EFGH$, name the preimage of each vertex of $EFGH$.

The preimages of E, F, G, and H are A, B, C, and D.

Each figure below has a preimage or image of isometry. Write the image of each given preimage.

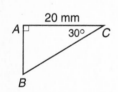

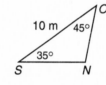

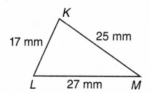

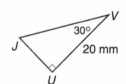

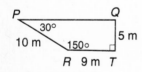

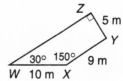

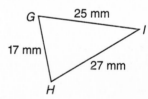

1. $\triangle ABC$ $\triangle UJV$

2. $\triangle DEF$ $\triangle SON$

3. quadrilateral $XYZW$
   quadrilateral $RTQP$

4. $\triangle LMK$ $\triangle HIG$

5. $\triangle MKL$ $\triangle IGH$

6. quadrilateral $TRPQ$
   quadrilateral $YXWZ$

7. Use a table of coordinates and the given figure to determine the coordinates of the image after a slide of 3 units up and a reflection across the y-axis. (-2, 7), (-4, 4), (0, 1)

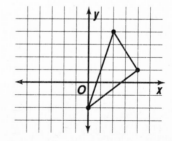

Geometry

Study Guide

Reflections

A **reflection** is a type of transformation that can be described by folding. If the diagram at the right is traced and folded along line ℓ, each point will coincide with its image. That is, A is mapped to D, B is mapped to E, and C is mapped to itself.

Note that each point and its image are on lines which are perpendicular to ℓ, the **line of reflection**. This line of reflection is also called the **line of symmetry**.

It is also possible to have a reflection image with respect to a point. In the figure at the right, Z is the reflection of X with respect to Y. The point of reflection, Y, is the midpoint of the segment drawn from X to Z.

For some figures, a point can be found that is a point of reflection for all points on the figure. This point of reflection is called a **point of symmetry**. A point of symmetry must be a midpoint for all segments that pass through it and have endpoints on the figure.

Examples:

1 Is the dashed line a line of symmetry for the figure?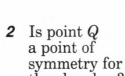

No, the two parts do not coincide if the figure is folded along the dashed line.

2 Is point Q a point of symmetry for the rhombus?

Yes, Q is a midpoint for all segments that pass through it and have endpoints on the figure.

Copy each figure. Use a straightedge to draw the reflection image of each figure over line m.

1.

2.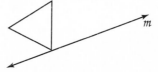

3.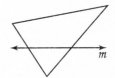

Determine if each figure has line symmetry, point symmetry, or both.

4.

5.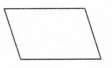

6.

7. Given $A(-1, 5)$ and $B(4, -2)$, graph $\overline{AB}$ on a coordinate plane. Then draw the reflection image over the line of reflection, the x-axis.

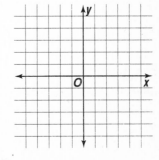

Geometry

Reflections

A **reflection** is a type of transformation that can be described by folding. If the diagram at the right is traced and folded along line ℓ, each point will coincide with its image. That is, A is mapped to D, B is mapped to E, and C is mapped to itself.

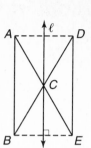

Note that each point and its image are on lines which are perpendicular to ℓ, the **line of reflection**. This line of reflection is also called the **line of symmetry**.

It is also possible to have a reflection image with respect to a point. In the figure at the right, Z is the reflection of X with respect to Y. The point of reflection, Y, is the midpoint of the segment drawn from X to Z.

For some figures, a point can be found that is a point of reflection for all points on the figure. This point of reflection is called a **point of symmetry**. A point of symmetry must be a midpoint for all segments that pass through it and have endpoints on the figure.

Examples: **1** Is the dashed line a line of symmetry for the figure?

2 Is point Q a point of symmetry for the rhombus?

No, the two parts do not coincide if the figure is folded along the dashed line.

Yes, Q is a midpoint for all segments that pass through it and have endpoints on the figure.

Copy each figure. Use a straightedge to draw the reflection image of each figure over line m.

1.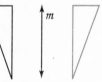

2.

3.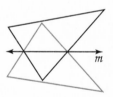

Determine if each figure has line symmetry, point symmetry, or both.

4.

line

5.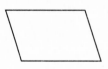

point

6.

both

7. Given $A(-1, 5)$ and $B(4, -2)$, graph $\overline{AB}$ on a coordinate plane. Then draw the reflection image over the line of reflection, the x-axis.

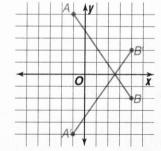

Geometry

Study Guide

Translations

A **composite of reflections** is the transformation that results from performing one reflection after another. A **translation** is the composite of two reflections over parallel lines.

Example: Draw the translation image of △ABC with respect to parallel lines *p* and *q*.

First draw the reflection image of △ABC with respect to line *p*. Then draw the reflection image of that figure with respect to line *q*. The translation image of △ABC is △FGH.

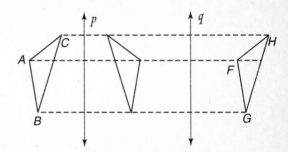

Notice that you can also think of a translation as a slide.

Draw the translation image of each figure with respect to ℓ and m. Assume ℓ ∥ m. Draw an X inside the translation image to identify it.

1.

2.

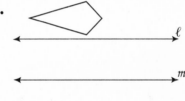

Use the figures below to name each triangle. Assume d ∥ e.

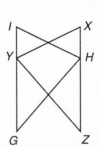

3. reflection image of △RST with respect to *d*

4. reflection image of △DEF with respect to *d*

5. translation image of △PQM with respect to *d* and *e*

6. Find the translation image of the figure with respect to the parallel lines *n* and *t*.

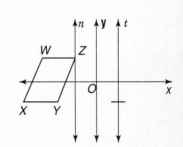

Translations

A **composite of reflections** is the transformation that results from performing one reflection after another. A **translation** is the composite of two reflections over parallel lines.

Example: Draw the translation image of △ABC with respect to parallel lines p and q.

First draw the reflection image of △ABC with respect to line p. Then draw the reflection image of that figure with respect to line q. The translation image of △ABC is △FGH.

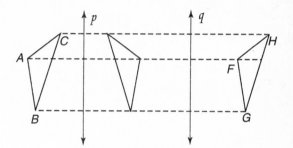

Notice that you can also think of a translation as a slide.

Draw the translation image of each figure with respect to ℓ and m. Assume $\ell \parallel m$. Draw an X inside the translation image to identify it.

1.

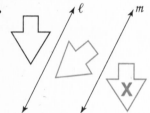

2.

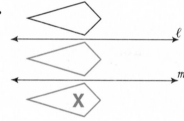

Use the figures below to name each triangle. Assume $d \parallel e$.

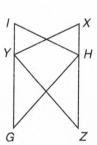

3. reflection image of △RST with respect to d △**PQM**

4. reflection image of △DEF with respect to d △**XYZ**

5. translation image of △PQM with respect to d and e △**IHG**

6. Find the translation image of the figure with respect to the parallel lines n and t.

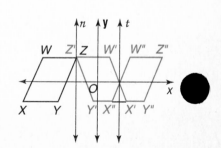

Rotations

The composite of reflections with respect to two intersecting lines is a transformation called a **rotation**.

Example: Draw the rotation image of *ABCD* with respect to lines *m* and *n*.

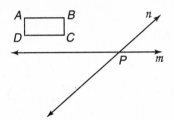 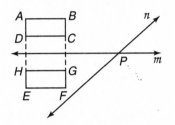 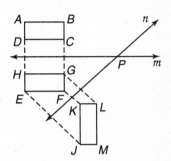

ABCD is on one side of *m* and *n*.

First reflect *ABCD* with respect to *m*. The image is *EFGH*.

Then reflect *EFGH* with respect to *n*. The image is *JKLM*.

Thus, JKLM is the rotation image of *ABCD* with respect to *m* and *n*.

Notice that *P* is the **center of rotation**. You can think of a rotation as a turn around point *P*.

The following postulate involves the measure of the angle of rotation.

In a given rotation, if *A* is the preimage, *P* is the image, and *W* is the center of rotation, then the measure of the angle of rotation, $\angle AWP$, equals twice the measure of the angle formed by intersecting lines of reflection.

Use a composite of reflections to find the rotation image with respect to lines s and t. Then state the measure of the angle of rotation.

1.

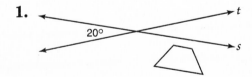

20°

2.

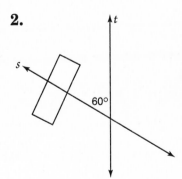

60°

84

Study Guide

Rotations

The composite of reflections with respect to two intersecting lines is a transformation called a **rotation**.

Example: Draw the rotation image of *ABCD* with respect to lines *m* and *n*.

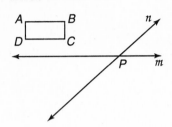 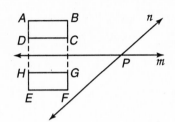 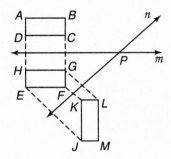

ABCD is on one side of *m* and *n*.

First reflect *ABCD* with respect to *m*. The image is *EFGH*.

Then reflect *EFGH* with respect to *n*. The image is *JKLM*.

Thus, JKLM is the rotation image of *ABCD* with respect to *m* and *n*.

Notice that *P* is the **center of rotation**. You can think of a rotation as a turn around point *P*.

The following postulate involves the measure of the angle of rotation.

In a given rotation, if *A* is the preimage, *P* is the image, and *W* is the center of rotation, then the measure of the angle of rotation, ∠ *AWP*, equals twice the measure of the angle formed by intersecting lines of reflection.

Use a composite of reflections to find the rotation image with respect to lines *s* and *t*. Then state the measure of the angle of rotation.

1.

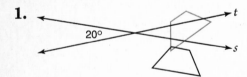

40°

2.

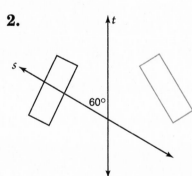

120°

Study Guide

Dilations

A **dilation** is a similarity transformation that alters the size of a geometric figure, but does not change its shape. In the figure below, the measure from the center C of dilation to a corresponding point on $\overline{RT}$ is three times the distance from C to a point on $\overline{AB}$.

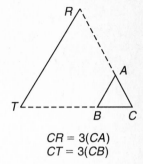

$CR = 3(CA)$
$CT = 3(CB)$

Thus $\overline{AB}$ with center C and a scale factor of 3 is enlarged to $\overline{RT}$. The following theorem applies to the above information.

Theorem 13-1	If a dilation with center C and a scale factor k maps A onto E and B onto D, then $ED = k(AB)$.

If $k > 0$, P', the image of point P, lies on $\overrightarrow{CP}$, and $CP' = k \cdot CP$.

If $k < 0$, P', the image of point P, lies on the ray opposite $\overrightarrow{CP}$, and $CP' = |k| \cdot CP$. **The center of a dilation is always its own image.**

If $|k| > 1$, the dilation is an enlargement.

If $0 < |k| < 1$, the dilation is a reduction.

If $|k| = 1$, the dilation is a congruence transformation.

Example: Given center C, find the measure of the dilation image XY if $AB = 4$ with a scale factor of $\frac{5}{4}$.

$XY = k(AB)$

$XY = \frac{5}{4}(4)$ Since $|k| > 1$, the dilation is an enlargement.

$XY = 5$

For each scale factor, find the image of A with respect to a dilation with center P.

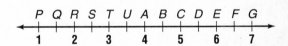

1. $1\frac{1}{2}$ 2. $\frac{1}{4}$ 3. $\frac{3}{8}$ 4. $\frac{5}{8}$

Find the measure of the dilation image of AB with the given scale factor. Then determine whether each dilation is an enlargement, a reduction, or a congruence transformation.

5. $AB = 3$, $k = 4$ 6. $AB = 1.3$, $k = 0.6$ 7. $AB = 12$, $k = -\frac{1}{4}$

8. $AB = 1\frac{5}{7}$, $k = \frac{3}{4}$ 9. $AB = 9$, $k = 1.0$ 10. $AB = \frac{5}{6}$, $k = -3$

NAME_____ DATE _____

Study Guide

Dilations

A **dilation** is a similarity transformation that alters the size of a geometric figure, but does not change its shape. In the figure below, the measure from the center C of dilation to a corresponding point on $\overline{RT}$ is three times the distance from C to a point on $\overline{AB}$.

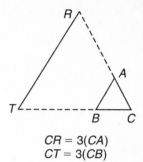

Thus $\overline{AB}$ with center C and a scale factor of 3 is enlarged to $\overline{RT}$. The following theorem applies to the above information.

$CR = 3(CA)$
$CT = 3(CB)$

Theorem 13-1	If a dilation with center C and a scale factor k maps A onto E and B onto D, then $ED = k(AB)$.

If $k > 0$, P', the image of point P, lies on $\overrightarrow{CP}$, and $CP' = k \cdot CP$.

If $k < 0$, P', the image of point P, lies on the ray opposite $\overrightarrow{CP}$, and $CP' = |k| \cdot CP$. **The center of a dilation is always its own image.**

If $|k| > 1$, the dilation is an enlargement.

If $0 < |k| < 1$, the dilation is a reduction.

If $|k| = 1$, the dilation is a congruence transformation.

Example: Given center C, find the measure of the dilation image XY if $AB = 4$ with a scale factor of $\frac{5}{4}$.

$XY = k(AB)$

$XY = \frac{5}{4}(4)$ Since $|k| > 1$, the dilation is an enlargement.

$XY = 5$

For each scale factor, find the image of A with respect to a dilation with center P.

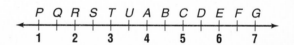

1. $1\frac{1}{2}$ **E**

2. $\frac{1}{4}$ **P**

3. $\frac{3}{8}$ **Q**

4. $\frac{5}{8}$ **F**

Find the measure of the dilation image of AB with the given scale factor. Then determine whether each dilation is an enlargement, a reduction, or a congruence transformation.

5. $AB = 3$, $k = 4$
   12, enlargement

6. $AB = 1.3$, $k = 0.6$
   0.78, reduction

7. $AB = 12$, $k = -\frac{1}{4}$
   -3, reduction

8. $AB = 1\frac{5}{7}$, $k = \frac{3}{4}$
   $\frac{9}{7}$, reduction

9. $AB = 9$, $k = 1.0$
   9, congruence transformation

10. $AB = \frac{5}{6}$, $k = -3$
   $-2\frac{1}{2}$, enlargement